Sex Life in Marriage

OPINIONS FROM THE MEDICAL AND SCIENTIFIC PRESS

"Will be found of value not only by married people but also by physicians who are called upon to give premarital examinations and advice in sexual hygiene."—*Health News* (Issued by New York State Department of Health)

"Scientific and practical. . . . Aims to bring about not only a happy sex life but harmonious home living and environment for children."—*American Journal of Psychology*

"This book is an unusually successful attempt to present the information about the ways in which love may be nourished and strengthened. All things considered, it is the best manual to give to persons about to be married and to those couples whose marriage threatens to fail because ignorance has prevented their love from growing and developing as God intended it should."—*Ohio State Medical Journal*

"Mr. Butterfield has discussed a difficult subject in a beautiful way. . . . A book which can safely be handed by physicians or ministers to any young man or woman who is contemplating marriage."—*American Journal of Digestive Diseases*

"This book is in line with modern sociological, psychological and medical thought on the subject."—*Science News Letter*

"The physician who is looking for an authoritative and well-written book to place in the hands of young married people will find this volume well suited for the purpose."—*Journal of the Iowa State Medical Society*

"The author, a member of the clergy, has combined excellently scientific truths with modern moral standards, and one cannot help but profit by reading this concise but informative treatise."—*Physiotherapy Review*

"Its wide distribution undoubtedly would prevent much unnecessary unhappiness."—*Archives of Internal Medicine*

THE courts of our country have wisely and generously sanctioned rational sex education. In the Stopes case (United States District Court) Federal Judge John M. Woolsey stated: "The book before me here has as its whole thesis the strengthening of the centripetal forces in marriage, and instead of being inhospitably received, it should, I think, be welcomed within our borders."

In the Dennett case (United States Circuit Court of Appeals) Federal Judge Augustus N. Hand found occasion to declare: ". . . The old theory that information about sex matters should be left to chance has greatly changed. . . . It may reasonably be thought that accurate information, rather than mystery and curiosity, is better in the long run."

SEX LIFE
IN MARRIAGE

OLIVER M. BUTTERFIELD, Ph.D.

FORMER STAFF MEMBER (CHILD DEVELOPMENT AND
PARENT EDUCATION) TEACHERS COLLEGE,
COLUMBIA UNIVERSITY

AUTHOR OF *Love Problems of Adolescence*, ETC.

Foreword by

SOPHIA J. KLEEGMAN, M.D.

FELLOW AMERICAN COLLEGE OF SURGEONS; ASSISTANT CLINICAL
PROFESSOR, OBSTETRICS AND GYNECOLOGY, NEW YORK
UNIVERSITY COLLEGE OF MEDICINE; ASSISTANT
ATTENDING GYNECOLOGIST, BELLEVUE
HOSPITAL, NEW YORK

Illustrations by

ROBERT L. DICKINSON, M.D.

PAST PRESIDENT, AMERICAN GYNECOLOGICAL SOCIETY

EMERSON BOOKS, INC.

NEW YORK

1951

MANUFACTURED IN THE UNITED STATES OF AMERICA

TO
ROBERT L. DICKINSON, M.D.

whose contributions to medical knowledge in the field of maternal health have been many and great; and who has inspired and assisted others to spread the medical and social knowledge essential to happy and wholesome family life.

THE AUTHOR

Dr. Butterfield was born in California in 1891, and for a number of years served as a Methodist pastor in the central and southern portions of the state. His success in dealing helpfully with adolescents', young people's, and parents' problems won for him the opportunity to do advanced research at Teachers College in New York City, where, from 1933 to 1935, he served as an assistant in the Department of Child Development and Parent Education. Upon publication of his dissertation on *Love Problems of Adolescence* in 1939, he was awarded the degree of Doctor of Philosophy by Columbia University.

Preceding this degree from Columbia, Dr. Butterfield in 1914 received a Bachelor of Arts degree from the University of Southern California, where he majored in philosophy. Thereafter followed a year's study at Drew Theological Seminary and another at the University of Southern California leading to his Bachelor of Divinity degree in 1916. He was then ordained a member of the Southern California Conference of the Methodist Church. Much later, in 1930, after specializing in family case work and social psychiatry at the University of Southern California, he was awarded the degree of Master of Arts in Sociology.

From 1918 to 1928 the author devoted a consider-

able proportion of his time to lecturing and consulta-
tion in the field of social and recreational leadership.
Out of this grew opportunities for counseling in preparation for marriage and in husband-and-wife relationships. Finding no satisfactory book available at
that time for instructing brides and grooms in the
sexual aspects of marriage, he prepared a pamphlet for
this purpose. It was immediately received with wide
favor by eminent persons in the fields of medicine,
social work, and religion, and by those administering
college courses on the subject of marriage and the
family.

In addition to the present work and the volumes already mentioned, he is the author of a number of
articles in *Reader's Digest, Parent Education,* and various religious periodicals.

In 1940, after having received his doctor's degree,
Dr. Butterfield returned to California, where he
served as instructor in sociology at the College of the
Pacific. Thereafter, for three years he was Chaplain of
California's model prison at Chino. During the war
years he served as Executive Director of the San
Diego Association for Family Living. Dr. Butterfield
is now a member of the faculty of Mt. San Antonio
College, Pomona, California, where he teaches psychology. He is a member-at-large of the Committee
on Marriage and the Home of the Federal Council of
Churches, a director of the Southern California section
of the National Conference on Family Relations, and
a member of the American Association of Marriage
Counselors.

PREFACE TO THE ELEVENTH PRINTING

This book was written for those, married or contemplating marriage, who wish to live wholesome and happy lives, and who realize they need detailed and reliable information to enable them to do so. Recent studies indicate that when both marriage partners have a fund of sound sex information, the prospects for successful marriage are greatly increased.

Indeed, some hundreds of readers of the present work have written the author to say that their own marriages have been greatly helped by the information contained in the work. They tell of reconciliations and happy adjustment after years of tension and frustration. Many express the intention of giving the book to friends, and to their own grown children, because they attribute to it so much of their happiness and success in marriage.

Authorities on the subject of human relations seem to have found worthwhile values in the book, as it appears with considerable frequency on recommended reading lists of libraries, churches, parent-teacher organizations, and college courses on marriage and the family. Also it is widely used and recommended by physicians, ministers, lawyers, educators, social workers, and psychologists; and journals in the fields of psychiatry, education, and health have endorsed it in gratifying terms.

As this new printing goes to press, the national divorce rate has soared to alarming heights, and broken families, with consequent ill effects on the children involved, are everywhere about us. It is the author's hope that this volume, together with informational writings by others who are qualified, will help to lower the incidence of divorce, and thereby help to keep homes intact. The book attempts to show how marriage may be made a more successful and attractive state than has heretofore been generally achieved.

The work grew naturally from the author's considerable experience over many years, as minister, marriage counselor, and teacher (as well as student) in the field of parent education. If the author has helped his parishioners, clients, and students, he has in turn learned much from them, and, accordingly, wishes here to express his gratitude and appreciation for all they have taught him.

OLIVER M. BUTTERFIELD

La Verne, Calif.
March 24, 1947

PREFACE

The conservation of wholesome family life is one of the most important objectives of educational and religious endeavor. This book has been written with the conviction that if monogamous family life is to continue to produce its rich returns in personal character and satisfaction, its weak spots must be strengthened and its spiritual values safeguarded against the inroads of materialism on the one hand, and asceticism on the other.

That the degradation of the sexual functions has been one of the weak spots in modern family life, no well informed person can deny. A child's inquisitiveness about any other phase of life is usually praised as a mark of mental alertness; his search for the truth about sex has been interpreted, all too often, as a sign of moral depravity. Young people have been well educated in nearly every other phase of life but left in almost complete ignorance about the most intimate of all personal relationships, that of sexual behavior in marriage. This refusal to face the facts has been one of the most prolific causes for divorce and strained relations between husbands and wives during the past hundred years.

Perhaps the most concrete proof of the value of

adequate sex education before marriage is the way in which young couples receiving such information tend to remain happily married, and the fact that couples with serious difficulties have been able to readjust their relationships when sexual conflicts were removed from the situation.

Many religious and high-minded people have had considerable difficulty, however, in acknowledging the propriety of printing such information in books. They would much prefer that any advice given be in the form of generalities and hints rather than in specific and detailed instruction. Many of them are still not quite sure that such guidance is in keeping with Biblical and ethical principles.

A broad survey of Biblical teaching will show little that is in conflict with the wholesome use of sexual enjoyment in marriage. Being one of the basic hungers of life, its normal satisfaction is generally approved and commended. The regular satisfaction of sexual desire between husband and wife is in no sense a "lust of the flesh," so long as it is used to promote and to express affection. Only when sexual passion becomes an end in itself, a coarse, selfish, all-absorbing concern, may it properly be given the name of "lust" and placed beside "gluttony" and "greed" as a degrading sin. The loving and unselfish use of this natural function is neither condemned nor forbidden by the Bible. Even the supposedly ascetic Saint Paul wrote the Corinthian Christians concerning marriage, saying:

"Do not withhold sexual intercourse from one another unless you agree to do so for a time in order to devote yourselves to prayers. Then come together again." *

The situation resolves itself down to the simple proposition, that if sexual intercourse is a proper and essential part of marriage behavior, then, by all means, let it be carried on in the most skilled and profitable manner possible and let due recognition be given to the part it plays in maintaining personal and social well being. For the maintenance of sexual harmony, it is apparent, is an all-important factor in strengthening the unity of marriage; and happy marriages, in turn, are essential to the stability of our social structure.

It would be too much to expect that any book might solve or explain all the problems of sexual adjustment in marriage. If this one can but indicate the possibilities for sexual satisfaction in marriage for the average couple, and direct those with peculiar and unusual difficulties to competent specialists, it will have accomplished the purpose of the author.

Special acknowledgments are due the many physicians, social workers, pastors, and married couples who have cooperated with the author in presenting the material in a form which might be practical and effective to the person seeking advice. Particular thanks are due those accomplished practitioners who compose the informal Round Table Discussion Group of the National Committee on Maternal Health.

* I Corinthians 7:5 Moffatt's Translation.

Their inclusion of the author in their group during the past two years has helped to give him something of the physician's point of view and to clarify certain ideas which previously were but conjectures.

Grateful acknowledgments should also be made to publishers and authors who kindly consented to have their works quoted in this volume; to Dr. Robert Latou Dickinson, of New York, for permission to use his diagrams as illustrations and for reading the manuscript and making helpful suggestions.

The material included here is based upon many years of first-hand experience as a marriage counselor, supplemented by a careful reading of the best literature in this field. The unusual, the abnormal, and the exceptional have been left to the medical and psychiatric specialists where they properly belong. Every effort has been made to include only what will be useful, practical, and well within the understanding of the average person.

OLIVER M. BUTTERFIELD.

CONTENTS

CONTENTS

xviii CONTENTS

FOREWORD

"So they were married and lived happily ever after."
THE END.

From our earliest childhood to our wedding day, has society ordained that we be left in the infantile stage of fairy-book concepts, and thus has it fostered the naïve expectation that following the marriage ceremony, happiness will be ours without effort or instruction. In this, our modern age, with the finest minds of the land and a great share of the country's wealth devoted to all the varied branches of knowledge and the manifold techniques of training, a most important phase of life—education for marriage—has been, with few exceptions, largely ignored or actively suppressed.

The remarkable achievements and accomplishments in all fields of scientific endeavor, the amazing, not to say miraculous, progress in every aspect of those mental efforts which have multiplied our material comforts—contrasted with the relatively slow betterment in human relationships makes a disheartening picture and shows once again that Man's worst enemy still is Man. In this continuous struggle between progress on one side and chaos on the other, is there no hope? Is it true that the power of evil is greater than the power of good? Or is there one power more potent than either good or evil, the terrifying and paralyzing power of ignorance? If this is so, does not our greatest hope lie in the oft proven fact that whenever the light of truth and knowledge is permitted to penetrate into the dark swamp of ignorance, the power of good is ever triumphant in the end?

The most urgent problem of our day is the improvement of human relationships. The most effective place to start this improvement is within the family unit. Harmony within the home is the very foundation of personal happiness, and a member of a harmonious family unit contributes happiness to all other human relationships.

All of us whose work deals with marital problems agree that lack of sexual harmony in marriage is the most frequent cause of disturbance or even disruption of family unity. This sexual discord is due, in the majority of instances, not to the faulty make-up of the partners, but to ignorance of the part each mate must play in order for both to achieve a normal and wholesome sex life.

"Let nature take its course" is a false and dangerous maxim to apply to the newly married couple. In the first place nature has not been allowed to take its course. Most men and women arrive at the marriage altar emotionally and psychologically handicapped by taboos, misinformation, carefully-instilled prejudices and false attitudes. In the second place, experience has shown us that failure has come too often to couples whose sole reliance has been on instinct.

The dangers of ignorance concerning the physical side of marriage have already become known to a sufficient degree to bring about an increasing demand for education in this field. To answer this demand, there has been a flood of literature so that the question arises as to the need of one more volume on this topic. For this particular book, however, the need is already a matter of proof. This work is an amplification of a pamphlet which has been received with such enthusiasm and has evidently filled so definite a hiatus that we know in advance the place it will fill and the welcome it will receive.

Oliver Butterfield is well qualified to write such a book. First and foremost, he personally has the background of a completely happy marriage. His training in psychology and sociology, as well as his experience of more than twenty years as pastor and family counselor, have given him an insight into the problems involved that few achieve. As a minister, he has united hundreds of couples. He has met their problems with open eyes and a sympathetic heart. He has too often seen the light of joy extinguished, but has in many instances been able to relight it, so that it burned more steadfastly and brightly than ever before. During his years of work as minister and marriage counselor, he has seen at close range the human tragedies, miseries, the irreparable damage to family units—which could so often have been prevented by a knowledge of the facts contained in this book. These facts he has stated wholesomely, truthfully, with clarity and candor; and they are in accordance with the best medical, psychological and sociological ideas of our times.

Our human problems are so many, our burdens so increasingly heavy—we must lighten the load, wherever we have the knowledge to do so. The spreading of knowledge to facilitate marital adjustment is one of our major social responsibilities; the withholding of this information one of the greatest social blunders that society can commit against those about to start married life.

This book will not enable every couple to "live happily ever after." Some marriages will fail because of economic difficulties. Others will fail because of the incomplete development of the two personalities entering into this relationship. Nevertheless, most marriages do start with love, and when failure results, this collapse is not so often for lack of love, as for want of the knowledge as to the ways in which love may be nourished and strengthened.

This book will answer many problems and, what is more important, a careful application of the knowledge herein contained will prevent many of these problems from arising at all. It is more especially for those about to be married or those recently married, that a clear understanding of this information transcends in value any other gift the pair can receive, for it will guide their steps toward that ideal—a completely happy marriage.

Sophia J. Kleegman, M.D.

CHAPTER I

MARRIAGE PATTERNS

Happy family life is the finest fruit of any civilization. In spite of confusing changes in economic, social, religious, and political life, domestic happiness is still the measure of national success the world around. Whatever detracts from the success, the stability, or the enjoyment of family life diminishes to that extent the happiness of the nation; whatever serves to make the relations of husbands and wives more wholesome, more enduring, and more vital, serves the common welfare and adds to the general social well-being. This fact holds as true for Patagonia and Russia as it does for America.

And yet, during the past generation, particularly in America, sexual maladjustment has been one of the outstanding factors contributing to an alarming increase in divorce and domestic unhappiness. The social and psychological causes of this situation are too numerous and too complex to be discussed briefly. With all our improvements in education reliable reports to the White House Conference showed that scarcely more than half of the children in modern American homes receive any instruction in sex matters from their parents. It is common knowledge that, until the last decade, most couples married

23

without having more than a smattering of reliable information as to the best experience of the race with respect to the most intimate aspects of marriage. The tragedy of this situation has been widely recognized and steps are now being taken to remedy it.

"It may be seriously questioned," reports the Department of Superintendence of the National Educational Association, "whether any other aspect of life causes more human misery in the United States today than do the maladjustments, repressions, frustrations, misunderstandings, physical disorders, and mental unbalance, growing directly out of failure to achieve the highest values in love, sex, and family life."

Dependence on silence and innocent ignorance as safeguards against immorality are slowly giving way to a confidence in the effectiveness of accurate facts presented by wholesome and high minded personalities. "The sex-impulses," declares Father Kirsch, "are too strong, the facts of sex are too widely known, and human curiosity is too great for the policy of silence to secure its end, even if ignorance were best. The very conditions that make it certain that our young people will get some sort of knowledge make it necessary that they should have it in the best possible form, without the over-emphasis either of neglect or of stress. The young people need the knowledge and are entitled to it."

The supplying of such information has become the concern of many religious and educational groups during recent years. Pope Leo XI issued an encyclical

"On Chaste Marriage" in 1930; the Federal Council
of Churches of Christ in America, representing more
than seventy-five per cent of the Protestant church
members, has long had an active standing committee
on Marriage and the Home which has not only furnished bibliographies on available literature but has
taken an active part in creating such literature and
in encouraging pastors and religious educators to
make suitable use of it. Public schools and colleges
are steadily improving their curricula in this field
and are ably supported by Parent-Teacher, Mental
Hygiene, Social Hygiene, Juvenile Protective, and
Family Welfare organizations. The day of complete
and wholesome frankness is not far off.

The sexual association of husband and wife,
throughout all ages, and among all peoples, has con-
stituted the essential and unvarying bond of marriage. In various cultures and at different periods in
the same culture, other factors, such as intellectual
comradeship, a desire for prestige, the need for a
satisfactory supply of domestic labor, or the desire
for an abundant progeny have entered into the arrangement; but as a rule, these factors are incidental to the more intimate physical association built
around satisfactions derived from sexual pleasure and
parenthood.

In one form or another most social and religious
groups have recognized the essential nature of the
sexual factor in marriage and have sanctioned and
protected it by appropriate laws and ceremonies. A
brief survey of some of the more common forms of

marriage in ancient and modern times may serve to show the importance of a well ordered sexual life in marriage and to give those who are disturbed about the changes now taking place in the outward forms of marriage a reasonable assurance that nothing is likely to change to any marked degree this inner and basic relationship between husbands and wives.

Matriarchal Marriage: The Mother Family

In its simplest, and possibly its earliest form, marriage was little more than a matter of temporary sex-mating. Among primitive tribes, and still recurring in modern society, as evidenced by frequent cases of unmarried mothers, a man and a woman met and had temporary sex relations. Afterwards, each went a separate way and if a child was born as a result of their union, the mother was left to care for it as well as for herself.

In some societies descent and kinship are regularly centered about the mother. The woman remains at home with her relatives and the husband comes to her. She retains her own name, her own property, and full control of her children. It is the husband who abandons his home and kindred to enjoy the benefits of the marriage relation. The woman's brother, father, or next male relative, rather than her husband, often becomes the actual guardian of her children. In such a family arrangement the husband is an officially recognized associate of the wife, but his economic obligations are less toward his wife than toward his mother and sisters.

Patriarchal Marriage: The Father Family

In direct contrast with this is the type of marriage where the man brings the woman to his home, gives her his name, and claims both her and her children as his property. The husband's authority in such marriages varies all the way from the right to kill or sell his wife, to where she is in most respects his equal before the law, both socially and economically.

In many backward parts of the world this patriarchal type of marriage is still the common form. In these places it is often the case that the man does not think of eating with his wife, much less will he be seen walking with her in public places. Rarely is she educated as he is, for little is expected of her except that she become the mother of his children, a worker in the home, and a means of sexual gratification to her husband.

In the more typical form of the patriarchal family, affection between the husband and wife was not an essential part of the marriage arrangement. While love sometimes developed out of mutual appreciation, it was not until long after the Middle Ages of the Christian era that love-marriages were common; and even yet they are not the universal pattern.

Polygamy and Communal Marriages

There are certain other forms of marriage and family life which are somewhat different from the monogamous marriages which are the dominant pattern in the Western world. While these various forms of multiple marriages are different from that based upon one man and one woman living together, the essentially sexual nature of the relationship is not greatly altered.

POLYGAMY embraces two types of multiple mating; *polygyny,* which is the situation where one man has several wives, and *polyandry,* where one woman has several husbands at the same time.

POLYGYNY is usually a type of patriarchal marriage, in which one husband has several wives living in the same community, though not always in the same single habitation. Among the Mohammedans and many of the African native tribes polygyny is common, though not universal. Westermarck, and others, have noted the fact that social custom requires in most such arrangements that the husband cohabit in turn with each of the wives so that no one of them may have cause for complaint. In the economically less favored cultures, polygyny often finds strong support among the women as a preferred industrial arrangement. Where wives do all the hard work it is a simple case of "many hands make light work." In wealthy and luxurious civilizations polygyny is more often a matter of sexual indulgence and a display of wealth.

POLYANDRY is a marriage arrangement where two or more men, often brothers, have one wife in common at the same time. Polyandry is, as a rule, related to social conditions where, as in Tibet, the struggle for existence is hard, and to divide up estates or to require that each son should set up a separate household would endanger the whole economic structure of family life. Among the Nairs of the Malabar coast in India polyandry exists even when the property is held in the wife's name, but the same fear of breaking up estates dominates the marriage form.

Compound or Group Marriage

At various times there have been societies where group marriages were a common form of family arrangement, in which several men were husbands to several women, with access to one another on the basis of mutual agreement for a limited time. In some cases these rights were exercised only when the chief or first husband was away. Among the Esquimaux, where men were gone for long periods on hunting or trading trips such an arrangement served both to provide a man with sexual consolation in the village where he chanced to be, and to keep the women left at home satisfied with their lot. Other groups have been organized on religious and eugenic principles. Notable among these was the Oneida Community which existed in New York State from 1848 to 1879 and where for thirty years was maintained a healthy and happy group life. The pressure of outside opinion finally forced them to give up their group marriage arrangements and conform to the prevailing customs.

In each of these types of marriage the fact to be noted is that its strength lies in the contentment of the husbands and wives with their social lot. If the arrangement has general social approval, and each partner feels that he or she is not being cheated, nor imposed upon, but is receiving his or her full share of the comforts and security of marriage, then the relationship may maintain itself in economic and emotional contentment. The difficulties of fulfilling such requirements under a polygamous or group system seem very great to those of us who have been reared in a democratic and monogamous tradition. In considering these systems, too, it needs to be kept in mind that the monogamous arrangement of one man and one wife is to be found side by side with the multiple arrangements. If one were forced to state an opinion it would probably be that these other systems and not monogamy were the deviations from the normal relationship.

Love-Marriages

With the break-up of the feudal estates in Europe, from the sixteenth century on, there was a gradual rise in the social life of the middle classes. Girls were educated as well as boys, and undesired marriages were not so often forced upon them. Parent-arranged unions gradually gave way to those planned by the young people themselves. The consent of parents was commonly sought, however, especially where there were important property rights to be preserved. On the whole, the general trend in most parts of the world has ever since been away from parent-dominated arrangements toward a freer choice of marriage mates on the basis of personal affection.

Opportunity for the girl to give or withhold her consent gave woman a new power in marriage, and has gradually increased her rights and authority in the home. In many parts of the world these developments are still in progress. Easy and widespread communication has hastened the trend toward making such free choices on the basis of mutual interest and affection.

This mutuality in marriage makes it less common for a woman to be merely the convenience of her husband. She insists on enjoying her share of the satisfactions of married life and is supported in this stand by public opinion. Marriage thus becomes a matter of the Golden Rule, with the husband no longer the sole chooser and the final authority. Such an arrangement makes possible a genuine partnership where work and pleasure, loving and being loved, are strictly mutual relationships.

This freedom of young people to choose their own partners for marriage has been accompanied by an almost universal tendency to set up a separate domestic establishment instead of living with either set of parents. Only during great economic stress does the usual modern couple deliberately choose to live with the parents. Thus, modern love-marriages tend to create a large number of new and small units of society. Under this system of marriage the husband and wife are more dependent upon each other for both economic and emotional satisfactions than under the older forms of family life. This circumstance makes it important that every phase of married living be as mutually satisfying as possible. In modern life there are few satisfactory escapes for the poorly adjusted couple; they must sink or swim on their own economic and emotional resources. If modern marriages are to be better than the more primitive types, couples must be prepared to see in their intimate associations something more than the blind compulsion of physical mating or the apathetic resignation which so often characterized the patriarchal family.

At its best marriage rises far above either of these alternatives. The more intelligent modern couple sees beyond the instinctive impulses, and beyond the need of food and shelter to the equally important needs of comradeship and mutual inspiration. Their sex experiences become for them not a selfish indulgence but a sharing of the whole personality. All that is worthy in the man and all that is good in the woman are poured into these intimate relationships with the result that the actual values are often far more spiritual and emotional than physical.

"This emotional characteristic of sex interest, when under discipline," says Sheldon, "renders available the whole energy resources of a personality as a sort of a vast reservoir for warming and enriching and supporting character. When out of discipline it can for the same reason devastate a personality almost as effectively and as quickly as can hunger or pain." *

* William H. Sheldon: *Psychology and the Promethean Will*, p. 112, Harper & Brothers, 1936.

Sexual relations must be reasonably happy in marriage or the entire arrangement is jeopardized. If pain or unhappiness comes out of the experience there is real danger that some form of blame will be attached to the other partner. Disappointment may give way to doubt, and this in turn to bitterness and complaint if further occasions prove equally unsatisfactory. Love and affection cannot possibly grow out of purposeless suffering and humiliation.

There are those who would discount the importance of sexual disharmony in marriage, saying in effect, that after all sex is but a small part of the total relationship, and that where it fails to satisfy, other things can easily be made to compensate for it. Practical observation by marriage counselors, domestic relations courts and physicians, however, do not bear out any such light estimate of its vital importance. Couples may differ in education, in religion, in many items deemed important in successful family adjustment and still the marriage can be a successful one. But without a considerable measure of sexual compatibility the whole marriage structure becomes a pretense and a disappointment.

In recent years, too, there has come a new appreciation of the inevitable tie between sex behavior and spiritual life. One need in no sense accept a Freudian philosophy of life to see that unless one's sex life is happily adjusted to his social life he is essentially a maladjusted, and spiritually a confused, or even a "lost" person. Instead of looking upon sex as a source of temptation and immorality many spiritually minded persons are now coming to appreciate the fact that it may be used in a positive and constructive manner so as to make a rich contribution toward spiritual living. This redemption of sex from the old taint of "carnality," from a destructive and degrading influence to one that is constructive and uplifting, bids fair to become one of the greatest moral achievements of the present generation.

CHANGES IN PUBLIC OPINION

Perhaps the most convincing evidence of the change in public opinion with respect to matters of sex is to be found in the modifications which the courts have made within recent years in the interpretation of the obscenity laws concerning the shipment of sex literature through the mails.

In a recent decision Federal Judge John M. Woolsey declared, "Whether or not the book is scientific in some of its theses is unimportant. It is informative and instructive and I think that any married folk who read it cannot fail to be benefited by its counsels of perfection and its frank discussion of difficulties which necessarily arise in the more intimate aspects of married life. . . .

"The book before me here has as its whole thesis the strengthening of the centripetal forces in marriage, and instead of being inhospitably received, it should, I think, be welcomed within our borders." (*United States* v. *Married Love*," 48 *Fed.* [2d] 821 [*Southern District of New York*, 1931].) A similar case, involving the question of whether a certain pamphlet was properly mailable or not, brought forth the following statement as a part of the decision:

"The defendant's discussion of the phenomena of sex is written with sincerity and feeling and with an idealization of the marriage relation and sex emotions. We think it tends to rationalize and dignify such emotions rather than to arouse lust.—It also may reasonably be thought that accurate information, rather than mystery and curiosity, is better in the long run and is less likely to occasion lascivious thoughts than ignorance and anxiety.—Any incidental tendency to arouse sex impulses which such a pamphlet may have, is apart from and subordinate to its main effect. The tendency can only exist in so far as it is inherent in any sex instruction and it would seem to be outweighed by the elimination of ignorance, curiosity and morbid fear. The direct aim and the net result is to promote understanding and self-control." (*Opinion of Judge Augustus N. Hand in United States* v. *Dennett, 39 Fed.* [2d] 564 [*Circuit Court of Appeals, 2d Circuit,* 1937].)

Therefore, without minimizing the religious, social, economic or other aspects of the marriage relationship we shall proceed to deal with its sexual problems in such a way that husbands and wives may come to see in the sexual aspects of marriage something beautiful and uplifting. No attempt will be made to distinguish between the "spirit and the flesh" for what the Creator has joined together in the human soul man's puny logic cannot put asunder. For good or for evil, the whole man and the whole woman go into the sexual experience. What comes out of it will depend on what art, what beauty, what affection go into it. We shall try to understand its emotions, its organic mechanisms, and those techniques of behavior, those attitudes of the mind which will produce the most desirable and inspiring effects upon husbands and wives. Not much will be left to the imagination, for an ignorant and wayward imagination can play havoc with the best intentions in the world. An intelligent imagination, aided by skilled instruction, can build to heights not commonly reached by the average person.

REFERENCES

Briffault, Robert, *The Mothers*, 3 Vols., Macmillan, N. Y., 1927. Vol. II, Chap. XIII.

Burgess, E. W., *The Adolescent in the Family*, Appleton-Century, N. Y., 1934, p. 470, also p. 193.

Committee on Marriage and The Home, *Ideals of Love and Marriage*, Federal Council of Churches of Christ in America, N. Y., 1932.

Dell, Floyd, *Love in a Machine Age*, Farrar and Rinehart, N. Y., 1930, Chaps. I and II.

Eastlake, Allan, *The Oneida Community*, George Redway, London, 1900.

Hamilton, G. V., *A Research in Marriage*, Boni, N. Y., 1929, pp. 531 ff.

Kirsch, Felix, M. O. M. Cap., *Sex Education and Training in Chastity*, Benziger Bros., N. Y., 1930, pp. 102-103.

Lowie, Robert H., *Primitive Society*, Boni & Liveright, N. Y., 1922, Chap. III.

Pope Leo XI, *"Concerning Chaste Marriage,"* encyclical issued December, 1930. Reprinted in *Readings on the Family*, Groves, E. R. & Brooks, Lee M. Lippincott, Chicago, 1934, p. 174.

Sheldon, William H., *Psychology and the Promethean Will*, Harpers, N. Y., 1936, p. 112.

Westermarck, E. A., *A Short History of Marriage*, Macmillan, N. Y., 1926, pp. 15-23.

Westermarck, E. A., *op. cit.*, p. 231.

Westermarck, E. A., *op. cit.*, Chap. X.

Tenth Year Book Department of Superintendence, National Educational Association, 1932, *Character Education*, p. 194.

CHAPTER II

SEXUAL ATTITUDES AND EMOTIONS

SEXUAL EMOTIONS AND EDUCATION

The mechanism by which a person is capable of participating in sexual activity and feelings is chiefly biological, organic, and inherited. The means by which this mechanism is set in motion is largely mental, psychological, cultural, and is determined by experience and training. In a particular form of society, such as that found in European or American life, we have long been trained to associate the nude body with matters of sex. So it comes about that in our culture, nakedness is generally found to be a sexual excitant. But among primitive peoples, who have never worn clothes, nudity is no more related to sex than a thousand other commonplace things in life, and so cannot exert a definitely sexual influence. The biological capacity for stimulation may be universal, but the psychological capacity for stimulation differs with the customs and mores of each social culture. What stimulates the sexual emotions of the Hottentot may have little or no influence on the European, and vice versa. It is of small value to discuss sex stimulation, therefore, without limiting such a discussion to a particular people and a specific culture pattern. Even within American life sex mores are so varied that what may apply to the rural, negro, or latin groups, may be vastly different from what is true for the New Englanders, the metropolitan sophisticates, or the college groups.

DIFFERENCES BETWEEN SEXES

Then too, there must be some limitation put on the use of the terms "maleness" and "femaleness" with respect to any very specific type of sexual response. Psychologists have tried to establish certain male and female types but so far have found that there is almost as much variation within either type as there is between them.

"It was found," says Stone in discussing one of the careful scientific studies of the sex drive in men and women, "that an excessively feminine score on the part of males or an excessively masculine score on the part of females is by no means always indicative of homosexual tendencies. In fact, the majority of such highly deviated scores are made by persons who showed no evidence whatever of inversion of sexual behavior. Marked deviation in the distinction mentioned, with respect to mental masculinity and femininity is probably only one of several factors which may act in various combinations with others to favor a development of homosexuality."

"Terman and Miles call attention to our almost complete ignorance as to what is desirable or undesirable with respect to mental masculinity and femininity. They are inclined to believe that the difference in male and female scores within a given sex, and perhaps also the intersex differences, are due mainly, if not wholly to environmental and educational as contrasted with the constitutional factors."

Novak takes the more traditional point of view but admits the same wide variation when he says: "Taken as a sex, there would seem to be no doubt that the sex feeling (libido sexualis) is much less highly developed in women than it is in men. There are a great many women in whom the sex drive is as strong as in any man, many in whom it is at least moderately developed, and some normal women in whom it is almost or completely absent.—An experience of thirty years has convinced me that there are many women who are physically and psychologically normal, who love their husbands devotedly, who live otherwise normal marital lives and perhaps bear many children, and who have never throughout their married lives experienced any degree of gratification from the sex act."

"The woman in whom a strongly developed sex sense has been planted has no reason to be ashamed of it, and unquestionably it is a strong factor in marital happiness. On the other hand, the woman to whom it is not vouchsafed is apt to worry about it a great deal, especially if this lack is resented by her husband."

It may well be said, therefore, that a woman is, in all probability, not less sexual than a man but rather that she has developed in our culture a different manner of expressing it. How much of this difference in the behavior of girls and women from men and boys may be accounted for by training and how much by native endowment cannot yet be determined.

The use of animal analogies and reports from so-called "primitive" societies furnishes us with nothing more than a possible clue to what might be true if we could segregate social and affectional influences from those that are strictly glandular and biological. Animals are concerned chiefly with the more or less seasonal instinctive urge to copulate and are apparently quite unmindful of any parental purpose or of the use of sex as a means of expressing affection. Their coming together is little complicated by either personal regard or public opinion; maleness and femaleness within the species is their chief concern. Jenkins found that the female white rat, during her period of heat, was fully as eager and willing to risk pain and difficulty as was the male to secure sexual satisfaction. Malinowski, reporting on the unhampered life of the south sea Trobrianders, showed that in most respects girls and girls' gangs were fully as aggressive sexually as were the boys. But again, all we can say is, that in this primitive society girls behaved in a manner more like boys than is true of American and European countries. How much of it was training and how much was feminine nature we cannot say with anything like scientific accuracy.

The more logical, and certainly the more practical conclusion is that sexual aggressiveness or sexual submission is much more a matter of individual personality than it is a matter of organic sex endowment.

There are extrovert women just as there are extrovert men and sociological and psychological case histories reveal women who are aggressive in matters of sex in about the same manner as men have been traditionally assumed to be. To assign to one sex or the other all aggressiveness or submissiveness is to do violence to many wholesome individual temperaments and to many happily married couples who have worked out an adjustment which is highly harmonious even though it may reverse the traditional pattern of sexual behavior in man and wife. Tradition has often made life all but unbearable for those who chance to differ from its self-imposed standards. Modern psychology gives to the non-average individual a new lease on life and happiness.

SEX STIMULATION

During infancy and the greater part of childhood sexual feeling is relatively slight and confined for the most part to the surface areas of the genitals. With the onset of sexual maturity during adolescence the nerves of the sexual organs have become sufficiently developed to involve emotions that are deeper and stronger and which include other areas of the body than the genitals themselves. The cardio-vascular system becomes intricately related to sexual ideas and sensations so that when the individual experiences any form of sexual stimulation the heart and circulatory system immediately proceed to put him or her in a state of organic readiness for sexual activity. This process begins on the involuntary level but may

be encouraged or wholly inhibited by the person involved when it reaches the conscious level.

Sexual emotions are aroused, as a rule, in one of
two ways: (1) by some form of pleasing bodily contact, or (2) by the influence of some mental image
derived from seeing, recalling, or imagining some
object or situation which has sexual significance.

Contact Stimulation

While practically any portion of the body surface
may be trained to respond as a part of a sexual pattern, there are certain areas which are much more
easily stirred than others. Besides the genitalia and
the areas immediately surrounding them, the lips,
breasts, thighs, ears, and neck are especially sensitive,
though not equally so in all persons. Close dancing,
passionate kissing, fondling, and embracing are common forms of contact stimulation.

Something more than simple contact is required to
produce sexual stimulation. There must be some sort
of psychological readiness, some degree of receptivity
before even the most intimate contacts can produce
a sexual reflex. In the presence of shame, fear, anger,
fatigue, or pain the very same contact which at one
time may produce a high degree of stimulation may
cause discomfort and sexual inhibition. When such
fears or unpleasant anxieties are present it is necessary to displace them before there can be any possibility of sexual interest.

Mental Stimulation

The mind exercises more control over sexual feeling than does any other factor in the human organism. While its control may not be absolute after well defined habit patterns have been set up through long years of repeated and similar experiences, nevertheless, it has been repeatedly shown that sexual habits are no less modifiable than any other habits. Precisely what is the relation between sexual imagery and sexual emotions is not clear, but it is well known that if one observes sexual acts, or recalls, or imagines such acts, or anything so closely related that it brings them into the stream of consciousness, then one experiences some measure of sexual feeling. If the sight or imagery is related to some experience which is highly charged with sexual feeling then the stimulation will be more intense. If its sexual significance is but slight in the experience of the individual then the excitation will be correspondingly slight. Observing the sexual behavior of birds or insects would ordinarily have much less significance than to observe the corresponding behavior of humans. A naked child exerts a very different influence on the average individual than a naked adult: the associated ideas make the difference.

Nudity, as has already been pointed out, is commonly associated in American and European life with sexual behavior and feelings. There was a time when the sight of a feminine ankle or leg resulted in an appreciable increase in heartbeats of the males who observed them. It was a part of the sexual mores of that generation. Nowadays all this has been greatly modified. Girls and women appear at the bathing beaches in garments which cover the breasts and trunk in only the flimsiest manner, leaving little to the imagination. While it can hardly be said that such dress is without sexual significance or that it is not responsible for considerable sexual stimulation on the part of the male observers, in general there has been a great change. Those young people who were born after the World War, particularly those in the more sophisticated metropolitan areas, will never know the mental suggestibility which troubled their parents and grandparents. This public acceptance of the one-piece bathing suit, and of the scantiest of trunks and brassieres in recent years is a clear demonstration of the way in which mental stimulation may be modified through familiarity.

One's first contact with a sexual idea and experience may often be more exciting than any subsequent contact. It is possible to become so accustomed to observing the breeding of live stock, the exposure of the genitals in medical practice, or of reading of seductions in some of the modern erotic literature that the experience loses its original power to stir one's feelings.

This modifiability of mental stimulation is a principle which is of particular importance in marriage. It may slowly undermine one's sexual appeal to his mate or it may steadily increase it, according to the degree or measure of satisfaction associated with it.

The diminishing influence due to familiarity with a given stimulus-object may be off-set by the recollection of the accumulated pleasures of the past or the anticipated satisfactions of the future in connection with the same person or object. The mind may go beyond the facts and, by creative enterprise, increase or reduce the stimulation. Expectancy builds up where familiarity breaks down. If the satisfactions of the past have been deep and genuine then the mere repetition of the stimulus can no more make them flat and meaningless than a cool drink of water is likely to become meaningless and insipid on a hot day, even though one has been drinking water all one's life.

Complex Stimulation

While it is possible to speak of contact stimulation and mental stimulation as separate entities, in actual experience they are seldom found in this simple state. Contact stimulation becomes meaningful only when one becomes conscious of it and by that time it is well on the way toward being mental stimulation. Mental stimulation can hardly exist without there being an early bodily response during which the erotic areas become receptive to pleasing contacts and tend, unless definitely inhibited, to remain unusually sensitive until displaced by a new idea.

In marriage this possibility of using one form of stimulation to re-enforce the other is of real practical value. It makes it possible for one mate to bring his companion to a desirable state of readiness much

more quickly and effectively than if he has to depend upon chance or upon either method alone. Or
when circumstances are unfavorable for sexual gratification it gives one a means of reducing any possible
stimulation to a minimum and by definite mental
control to behave in a manner which will have no
undesirable after-effects.

DIFFERENCES IN TEMPERAMENT

There are persons with more or less imaginative
and poetic temperament who do not respond readily
to contact stimulation until they have first been excited by some form of mental imagery, or romantic
love play. To approach them by any direct and
abrupt procedure is to find them cold and unresponsive. It is most often a woman of this type married
to a husband who does not appreciate her peculiar
needs who is surprised to find herself tremendously
aroused and infatuated by the attentions of some
attractive male acquaintance. The precise reverse is
true of many men whose unimaginative wives prefer
either to avoid sexual relations as far as possible, or
to engage in them with a passivity which makes the
experience an insipid and distasteful affair.

These more artistic and poetic individuals often
find peculiar delight in perfumes, in dainty clothing,
soft lights, lovely music, or in the great out of doors.
Reading a romantic novel, seeing a sexually suggestive play, or dancing to the rhythm of sensuous
music is a far more effective means of stimulating
them than is any form of direct contact. The intelli-

gent use of such devices may often make the difference between success and failure when it comes to pleasing and satisfying one's husband or wife. Some careful observation of responses under various circumstances, and possibly, a frank discussion of likes and dislikes in such matters, will serve to let each partner know what sort of preparation is most acceptable and what best prepares each for a mutually satisfying experience. The discovery of these important factors is one of the opportunities of the honeymoon period, but it should be given continued attention throughout married life.

SEXUAL AWAKENING

It may happen occasionally that a girl will come to marriage without having been pointedly aware of sexual feelings, but it does not follow that she is for that reason incapable of them. In most instances it is merely a matter of providing the proper expectation and the necessary stimulation. Kissing, caressing, and all forms of close bodily contact with her lover are the natural means of arousing her sexual feelings. Such women, and others who bring to marriage some long established fear of marital intimacies, may experience considerable difficulty in responding fully to the husband's courtship, but if he is sympathetic and understanding he will rarely fail to overcome her inhibitions within a short time and help her to become fully responsive.

During adolescence and before there has been any experience of complete sexual relations, erotic emotions tend to occur as vague, body-wide and inarticulate feelings. Subsequently, as the individual experiences more and more such feelings, they come to be associated in the mind with specific persons, objects, or ideas. This definition and localization of sexual emotions is one of the marks of sexual maturity. It is quite possible that the restrictions thrown around girls in our society tend to keep many of them in something of an adolescent state of undeveloped sexual emotionality longer than is usually true of boys. This fact may explain why there are some brides who are not so much inhibited in matters of sex as simply unawakened. Within the protection and security of a happy marriage this "sexual awakening" is much less likely to be a damaging experience than is often the case in the premarital experimentation of impulsive and uninformed youth.

Attention is called by various writers in this field to the fact that the husband is usually the more quickly aroused to the full pitch of sexual passion than is the wife. In most cases this seems to be true but not always, and if not, it is a matter of no great concern. Here again, individuals have a right to differ without being at all concerned about the rule of averages. In any given combination of personalities in marriage it is simply necessary for the couple to discover through experience what is the usual method or rate of response and then adapt procedures to it.

Not every person, however, responds in exactly the same way on every occasion. Fatigue, worry, or some general but much less definable emotional state may account for such variation. If couples will be observing of each other in these respects they will find out how they may increase or decrease the intensity of their sexual feeling with considerable skill. This is an important factor in determining happiness in marriage for there are times when sexual emotions must be held in check as well as others when they need to be stimulated in order to please one's mate.

THE VALUE OF CARESSING

A woman's love of being caressed is not necessarily connected in her mind with sexual intercourse. She may love to be caressed without any thought of continuing on to full sexual expression. Happy is the wife whose husband knows how to make love to her without causing her to suspect a selfish motive. Caressing is often a good thing in and of itself and quite apart from being a preliminary to sex intercourse.

Many men come to marriage with more sexual experience of one sort or another than their wives. Sometimes they are too impulsive and tend to hurry their brides into this experience without adequate preparation. Unless she is positively fearful of venturing into the new experience the wife will appreciate an ardent show of affection, provided he is gentle and tender through it all.

"Ordinarily the preliminaries to intercourse and the conduct of it should follow certain well recognized principles which take cognizance of the aggressiveness of the male, and of his imperious, quickly aroused, rapidly culminating passions, and of the quiescent, slowly aroused nature of the female, whose passions are usually brought to concert pitch only by much courting and many tender caresses. . . . A woman craves always, from puberty to senility, hand-clasps, soft looks, embraces, kisses, love, and appreciation. Courtship must be continuous after marriage if she is to be happy and her husband is to be transfigured. Courting after marriage should be like courting before marriage, only it should be raised to the hundredth power." (W. F. Robie, *Sex and Life.*)

EMOTIONS THAT HINDER

Few people come to marriage without some sort of hindering fear. Because sex has been such a mysterious thing through the ages, many taboos and warnings have been built about it for purposes of social protection. Shame, guilt, the fear of pain, the fear of pregnancy, and various anxieties with respect to the ability to perform the sex act properly all serve to make success difficult. Many husbands and wives do not know how to do away with these fears which frequently grow until they become the causes of broken homes. The proper instruction of brides and grooms before marriage can prevent most of these difficulties.

Shame

Misguided and insufficient sex instruction during childhood leads many persons to look upon all sex acts as something obscene. Years of repression and the constant attitude of shame toward all sex manifestations make it difficult for some brides to experience any other emotion when contemplating sexual affairs. Scoldings, punishment for inquisitiveness concerning sex, for appearing naked, or for playing with the sexual organs, or permitting others to do so, very often result in the establishment of these tragic mental attitudes early in childhood. Unless they are changed before marriage it is exceedingly difficult for one to respond as he or she ought to the normal contacts with his or her marriage partner.

Guilt

Where a sense of shame has been built up during childhood it naturally follows that any transgression of rules against sexual familiarities is likely to promote a sense of guilt and a fear of detection. Many married people confess that although they are aware of the fact that there is no rule against such relations within marriage, they nevertheless find great difficulty in thinking of such indulgence without embarrassment. There are some husbands and wives who cannot talk to one another about their sexual feelings without a great sense of shame and guilt. Often it is so great that it makes any intelligent explanation of their difficulties practicably impossible.

Whenever a bride finds that she cannot throw off these fears of childhood and share gladly in the courting which leads to sexual relations, it will help greatly if her husband will patiently retrace with her the events connected with the creation of these fears. When both come so to know and understand them, however serious or innocent their nature, they may be left behind and a new and fearless attitude developed which is more suited to the needs of married life.

The Fear of Pain

The discomforts of married life have been so much overemphasized by unhappy wives that many girls come to marriage with needless anxieties about it. They may have read of masculine brutality, of the necessity of enlarging the vaginal opening during the first intercourse, and of unusual difficulties in childbirth. Such things serve to unnerve them as they approach the marriage bed and make them much more fearful than the facts warrant. Not all women worry about such things, but some do and it is important that these be helped to know that most natural functions of the body are attended by some degree of pleasure. None of these functions are capable of producing greater pleasure than proper sexual intercourse between true lovers. Only in unusual cases is there any considerable discomfort and by the exercise of proper forethought even this may be largely avoided. It is becoming more and more a common practice for couples to have a complete premarital physical examination by a well informed physician so that no such difficulty may be encountered during the honeymoon. In a subsequent section the important details of such an examination will be more fully explained.

Inferiority Anxieties

Now and then persons develop anxieties about the hymen, the size of the penis, the fullness or the sensitiveness of the breasts, or about some other bodily characteristic in which they may differ from others of their acquaintance and conclude therefrom that they may have difficulty in properly performing the marital act. In exceptional cases some of these conditions may possibly cause trouble, but until this has been actually established by careful examination it is foolish to make any premature assumptions. Practically, it will be found in most instances that, within a rather wide range, the size of the sexual organs has relatively little to do with their effectiveness. Their sensitiveness, their functional vigor, and the intelligence with which they are used are much more important in determining success and happiness. The occasional couple who does encounter difficulties of a structural nature, or some unusual disproportion in size of their organs, will usually find it possible to obtain from a skilled physician or counselor such instruction as will make possible a satisfactory adjustment. With all that is now known concerning such matters there is no reason why the false modesty which handicapped some of our parents should continue to afflict the present generation and cause to be withheld from them the advantages of modern medical and psychological skill.

The Fear of Pregnancy

Most couples desire children but they do not wish them too soon or too often. Where the fear of pregnancy exists it is exceedingly difficult for a woman to enter into the lovemaking which may lead to sexual intercourse with the joyful abandon so vital to success and satisfaction. But if husband and wife love each other sincerely, sight, sound, and touch all combine to bring pleasant hopes and memories into consciousness and the repression of sexual desire becomes an unnatural and an oppressive thing. Except temporarily, for reasons of health, most authorities agree that no couple should attempt to abstain from sexual relations in marriage. The spiritual, as well as the physical benefits of sexual relations gladly shared, far outweigh any possible benefits of discipline through sexual abstinence. Because proper sexual intercourse does contribute so much toward the growth and development of mutual love, it would be unfortunate indeed if it had to be limited to those relatively few occasions when children were desired. Furthermore, most couples wish a few months' time to become fully acquainted and personally adjusted in various ways before their affairs become complicated with preparations for the coming of a baby.

For this reason every couple should talk over, *before marriage,* the various economic and health factors which might influence their preferences as to the number, and spacing, of children. On the basis of this understanding they should adopt some mutually satisfactory plan of family limitation or child spacing with a view to conserving the resources of the entire family. For where the family is large and the income low, the strain on the budget is great and has far-reaching effects. The deprivations in food, clothing and medical care affect both children and parents; the educational opportunities of the children are limited; the mother's nervous system is strained by the insistent claims on her attention; and her strength is sapped by too frequent pregnancies. A well trained physician can suggest one or more methods of contraception which are highly dependable and which in no way endanger health or happiness.

ATTITUDES AND EMOTIONS THAT HELP

Affection

A strong mutual affection between husband and wife is one of the basic essentials of a lasting and satisfactory sexual relationship. While it is conceivable that such intimacies might be temporarily satisfactory on the basis of mere romantic experimentation, it requires a deeper and more lasting attachment to make its repetition through the years a continuing source of happiness. To enter upon this most intimate of all relationships with anything other than a deep and sincere affection for one's partner is to handicap one's self from the start.

Love has a way of seeking to express itself through physical channels. The giving of gifts, the saying of "sweet nothings," sitting close to each other, holding hands, hugging and kissing, are all manifestations of this fundamental characteristic of personal affection. It will be observed, however, that as love grows more and more intense, these common forms of expression seem less and less adequate to convey the depths of love which is felt one toward the other.

More kisses and yet more passionate kisses fail to express what lies within. Something still more expressive is the inarticulate longing of all true lovers.

That there is such a supreme and satisfying physical expression of affection between man and wife, and that this includes the full sexual embrace, is quite beyond the comprehension of some brides. Unfortunate training has led them to believe that sexual relations are something wholly apart from love and only to be endured as a means of having children or to gratify the selfish desires of a passionate husband. They seem quite unaware of the fact, rightly understood and properly entered into, sexual intercourse is an exquisitely delightful experience for *both* husband and wife. Nothing in all their married fellowship will contribute more toward their growth in love and their sense of spiritual oneness than this beautiful and sacred contact.

Havelock Ellis well points out that the art of love, "is far from being confined to the physical aspects of love. There is here an art, and a difficult art, even when physical love is not directly concerned, or when it has fallen into the background, or when physical relationships do not take place at all. The recognition of individual freedom, the allowance for differences of tastes and disposition even when there is fundamental unity of ideals, the perpetual call for mutual consideration, the acceptance of the other's faults and weaknesses with the acknowledgment of one's own, and the problem of overcoming that jealousy which because it is rooted in Nature every one has in some form and at some time to meet—all these difficulties and the like exist even apart from sex in the narrow sense. Yet they are a large part, even the largest part of the art of love. Every failure here may become a source of misery or of weakness in the whole art of living."

Confidence

Confidence is the natural outgrowth of love and certainty. To be sure that one's husband or wife is doing his or her best under all circumstances to reach a common goal is a strengthening and an inspiring thing. Whatever improves confidence helps to make sexual relations more successful in marriage; whatever undermines confidence is a dangerous and a damaging thing. Even the slightest deceptions are fraught with dangers for they often give rise to groundless suspicions which months of repentant living cannot wholly wipe out. Love and happiness can thrive only in an atmosphere of complete trust and confidence.

Interest and Enthusiasm

Whenever two people have mutual interests and are enthusiastic about them it takes much to make them fail of their objectives. While there may be times when their interests may not be equally intense, if there is love and confidence these will tend to balance the situation and make possible genuine and effective cooperation. Interest has in it the element of expectancy and alertness which makes it possible to note even slight improvements in circumstance. In matters of sexual adjustment small things are often of special importance. The wife must be interested in the husband's reaction and the husband in the wife's. They must learn to indicate by word or sign how they feel and what they wish with regard to the attainment of their satisfactions. Where there is interest and enthusiasm there is every chance of success.

Patience

It has already been said that successful sexual adjustment between husband and wife is rarely, if ever, attained immediately upon marriage. More often it requires time, but, if the partner be otherwise desirable, it is well worth all the patience it takes to achieve it. Patience is not a dumb resignation, passive, inert and helpless. It is rather that relaxed readiness to take advantage of the right mood at the right moment and push on to success. It is the courage to try repeatedly what may have failed utterly before. It is the refusal to be angry when things turn out less well than was expected or when for some reason one's partner does not come quite up to expectations. True patience may accomplish at the fiftieth trial what impulsiveness and temper could never do.

Sympathy

Sympathy is a word derived from the Greek and means "to feel with," and as such has a very important place among the attitudes and emotions favorable to sexual harmony. It involves the attempt on the part of each mate to appreciate how the other feels, and to cooperate in working toward what will be a pleasing experience for both. The successful lover, man or woman, is such, not because he demands this favor or that of his beloved, but rather, because he makes himself appreciated and supremely desired by the way in which he accommodates the moods and wishes of his companion. To anticipate the wishes of one's beloved, to create and fulfil an expectancy of delight is the essence of romance and chivalry. In no relationship is sympathy more applicable and appreciated than in those instances where the wife is for the time unable to secure the pleasing relaxation which follows a satisfactory orgasm in sexual intercourse. It is equally important when, because of some unusual sensitivity, the husband's ejaculation comes sooner than he wishes and he is unable to properly play his part. True sympathy is evidenced by an honest attempt to assist the other person in every way possible to accomplish the desired purpose.

Playfulness

To speak of the intimate sexual relations of marriage as a form of play may seem highly improper to some persons, but if they will think the matter through a bit further it will not be difficult to consider them in that light. Certainly, sexual intimacies at their best are not work, and any strained and serious tension connected with them serves to rob them of their spontaneity and their uplifting quality. "Sexual pleasures, wisely used and not abused," says Havelock Ellis, "may prove the stimulus and liberator of our finest and most exalted activities."

At their best, sexual relations in marriage are certainly a form of mutual relaxation and enjoyment. Those couples who come to regard them as a form of exalted play are the ones who find in them that mutual joy and contentment which is the object and the goal of all true marriages. Play in its finest sense is not a wild orgy of reckless sensuality, wholly unmindful of the decencies of life, but rather that freedom from compulsion, that spontaneity of action which makes an activity refreshing, inspiring, and uplifting. Certainly these experiences should not be looked upon as obligations and as duties, to be soberly and solemnly performed. Rather are they happy occasions of giving and sharing the delicate and intimate pleasures of bodily intimacy with one's beloved. This is play at its highest and its finest development. To speak thus of sexual behavior is not to degrade it but rather to lift it above that concept of shame and indecency which has overshadowed it for so many generations. "You have made the sexual relations of marriage beautiful" is the comment written by hundreds who have been given this feeling about the intimacies of married living in the course of the author's consultations and correspondence.

REFERENCES

Allen, Edgar, *Sex and Internal Secretions*, Williams and Wilkins, Baltimore, 1932. Chap. XVIII, "Sexual Drive," by Calvin P. Stone, p. 876.

Ellis, Havelock, *Psychology of Sex*, Emerson Books, 1938, p. 351.

Jenkins, M. T., *The Effects of Segregation on the Sex Behavior of the White Rat as Measured by the Obstruction Method*, Genetic Psychological Monographs, 1928, 3, 457-571.

Malinowski, B., *The Sexual Life of Savages in Northwestern Melanesia*, Horace Liveright, N. Y., 1929, 2 Vols. Vol. I, pp. 261-273.

Novak, Emil, *The Woman Asks the Doctor*, Williams and Wilkins, Baltimore, 1935, pp. 182-183.

Robie, W. F., *Sex and Life*, pp. 358-359, *Passim*.

CHAPTER III

THE ORGANS OF SEX

Because the organs of sex and the emotions connected with them operate in response to rather specific stimuli, it is necessary to know a good deal about their structure and function if the happiest results are to be obtained in the marriage relationship. Each person should understand not only how his own organs operate and respond to stimulation, but should have the same knowledge concerning those of his mate.

THE WOMAN'S SEX ORGANS

The sex organs of the woman are mostly enclosed within her body. As may be seen by the accompanying diagrams, they consist principally of the vulva, the vagina, the uterus, and the ovaries. The breasts are also a part of her sex apparatus but for most purposes they need not be considered in the same groups with the other organs. In some women they are very sensitive to caresses, even to the point of orgasm.

The vulva is the collective name for all the external female sexual parts lying between the pubic eminence in front and the anal opening near the back of the crotch. These include the large, rounding outer lips (labia majora), the smaller inner lips (labia minora), the clitoris, the lubricating glands, the erectile bulbs, and the meatus which is the external opening of the urinary bladder.

The two larger rounded folds run from the pubic eminence (the mons), down between the thighs, on either side of the vulvar cleft, nearly to the anal opening. Like the mons above, their outer surfaces are covered with hair somewhat finer in texture but usually about the same color as that of the head. These folds, when drawn apart, present an oval opening with sloping sides, about two inches from front to back and two and a half inches deep, with the hymen, and the meatus on the flattened base of this depression. This area is called the vestibule and one of its purposes is to guide the penis into the vagina.

At the front and upper end of the oval opening is a highly sensitive prominence about the size of a pea, covered by a movable fold of skin. This prominence is the clitoris. Its rounded tip is a miniature of the end of the penis, except that it has no excretory passage. The surface is furnished with an extraordinary number of nerve endings. In some women the clitoris increases considerably in size and firmness during sexual excitement, in others there is little or no change. The amount of enlargement (erection), like the range in size, has little relation to its capacity for sensation. To the surface of the visible part of the clitoris, called the glans, the foreskin or prepuce may be adherent, and this sometimes handicaps sensation and occasionally shuts in white particles of shed surface cells, with consequent irritations. Cleansing beneath the prepuce is nearly as much a routine care for some women as for men.

The two smaller lips, the labia minora, extend from the prepuce and the clitoris backward on either side of the vestibule. These are of delicate skin, except the deeper parts of the inner surface, where, like the vestibule, hymen, and vagina, they are covered with soft mucous membrane resembling that of the mouth.

A thin crescent or tiny curtain of membrane, called the hymen, partly covers the opening to the vagina. It lies in folds, with the gap in front; the aperture in virgins spreading to an inch in diameter, allowing passage of the menstrual blood or the nozzle of the douche. In most women the membrane is thin and somewhat elastic, in a few thick and resistant, while occasionally the opening is tiny and exceedingly sensitive. Thus an opening that normally admits an adult forefinger, requires stretching before the penis can pass, else, if entered quickly, will suffer one or more small nicks or notchings, with resultant pain and a little oozing. The usual description of this process as "rupture," "tearing," or "destroying" is thoroughly misleading and alarming. Apprehension may bring contraction or spasm of the muscles that shut the lower end of the vagina, adding to the resistance and distress.

In the case of a hymen not acutely tender and fairly elastic, with the assistance of good lubrication and strong desire, entry can be made with little pain;

but there is much difference in this regard, and possible suffering and dread should be avoided. Gradual preliminary stretching for a few days, when needed, effects this.

At the sides and base of the hymen are the minute openings of two glands which secrete a clear mucus. This is poured out during sexual excitement, lubricating and facilitating the entry of the male organ and enhancing the pleasure in motion.

The vagina is a very elastic canal running up from the hymen to where it connects with the uterus. Normally, it is about three and a half inches long, but so elastic and movable are the surrounding tissues that under sexual excitement the total passage may be stretched to a depth of nearly six inches without discomfort. An occasional woman may find her vagina is short and she may require some special advice as to positions in intercourse in order to avoid discomfort during sex relations.

The uterus is a muscular-walled organ, smaller than a woman's fist and similar in shape to a flattened pear. It is suspended by elastic, slightly muscular ligaments from the surrounding organs and body walls. Its lower and smaller end, the cervix, connects with and extends down into the vaginal canal for a half inch or more. The lower opening of the uterus is in the rounded cervix and is called the external os, or mouth. Before the experience of childbirth it is usually not larger than a broom straw in diameter, but after childbirth it becomes somewhat larger and does not close up as completely as before. It is through this opening that the sperm cells must pass to reach and fertilize the ovum in the upper end of the Fallopian tubes. The normal uterus tips forward almost at right angles to the vagina and lies suspended above the urinary bladder and beneath the intestines. During pregnancy the firm muscular walls of the uterus expand and grow until the cavity becomes nearly a foot long and about six or seven inches in diameter. It takes about six weeks after childbirth for the uterus to return to its normal size and condition.

The ovaries are smaller in size than the testicles and are located to the right and left of the upper end of the uterus, about two inches above and back of the pubic bone. These glands produce the ova, or egg cells which, when matured, are discharged near the open end of the Fallopian tubes. These tubes are attached to the upper end of the uterus on either side and curve in around the ovaries, opening out in something of a funnel shape near the external surface of the ovary. When the ripened ovum separates from the ovary it moves up into the open end of the tube and is ready for fertilization. Should no sperm cell succeed in penetrating its outer shell it dies within the day and is absorbed or dissolved.

If fertilization does not take place, after a certain time the blood vessels on the inner walls of the uterus commence to ooze, some of the surface tissue comes away, and this bloody discharge, known as menstruation, passes out through the vaginal cavity. In most healthy women, this discharge continues for a period

of from three to five days and recurs from month to
month at fairly regular intervals from puberty to
between the age of forty and fifty years, after which
it gradually ceases. Kopp reports approximately 80
per cent of 7610 cases in which the periods recurred
at "regular" intervals, leaving about 20 per cent
which were "irregular" as to the date of their recur-
rence. Various reports have been given as to the
length of the monthly cycle and the proportion of
healthy women who vary somewhat from the usual
interval of 28 days. Kopp found that 65.7 per cent
of her cases reported the usual interval of 28 days,
but that 26.4 per cent had a longer interval and 7.5
per cent a shorter one, the extremes running all the
way from 12 to 63 days. Provided the woman is
healthy and feels well there need be no concern over
the fact that her menstrual periods do not follow the
average pattern.

A few women experience considerable pain or
discomfort for a day or so at the beginning of
the period. They find it advisable to avoid strenuous activity and extremes of heat and cold. Other
women experience practically no discomfort and
are able to pursue their usual activities with no
particular inconvenience. Murrell reports a study
covering 6,099 girls in England where only two per
cent suffered severe pains and more than half "suffered no pain of any sort" during menstruation.

When conception has taken place, and the fer-
tilized egg starts to grow within the uterus, menstruation ceases for the remaining months of

pregnancy. Following childbirth it may be delayed during the entire time the child is being nursed at the breast, but in some women it is resumed within a short while.

THE MAN'S SEX ORGANS

A man's sexual organs consist of the *penis* and *testicles* outside the body and several important glands inside the body. The penis is a soft, spongy, cylindrical body from four-fifths to one-and-a-fifth inches in diameter and from three and a half to four inches in length when hanging relaxed beneath the pubic bone. Its outer extremity, called the *glans,* or head, is slightly larger than the main body and is abundantly supplied with nerve endings which are very sensitive to heat and touch. At birth there is a fold of loose skin, known as the prepuce or *fore-skin,* covering the glans and unless removed by the operation called *circumcision,* remains through life. Sometimes this fold of skin is not properly cared for during childhood and continues to adhere to the glans as the child grows to manhood. In such cases it cannot be slipped back so as to leave the entire glans bare and tiny flakes of shed lining, called *smegma,* collecting between it and the surface of the glans tend to produce irritation and an ill-smelling odor. In other cases the outer opening of the fold is so small that it cannot be stretched sufficiently to permit the glans to be fully uncovered. If the fore-skin adheres or the opening is too small, it should be attended to by a physician before marriage.

Under ordinary conditions the penis hangs limp and soft below the pubic bone and the man is quite unconscious of it. Sexual excitement, however, causes a rush of blood into the porous storage tubes of the organ and the nerves controlling the blood vessels prevent it from escaping, so that the resulting pressure within the walls of the penis cause that cylinder to become firm and very rigid. This stiffening, or *erection*, causes the organ to extend at an acute angle from the upper body while increasing its length to about six inches and its diameter to about an inch and a half. In different individuals the length or the diameter of the penis may be more or less without in any way affecting its capacity in sexual relations. If sexual excitement is slight or temporary the flow of blood to and from the penis is so balanced that the organ becomes again soft and loses its sexual sensitiveness. Stiffening is essential to make possible insertion of the penis into the vagina during sexual intercourse.

The *testicles* are two firm, oblong glands enclosed in a soft flexible sack (the *scrotum*) that hangs underneath the penis in the groove formed by the thighs. These are the glands that produce the male germ cells (the *spermatozoa*) that are injected through the penis into the vagina of the woman during intercourse. The spermatozoa mature in the testicles and epididymis and find their way up through the *vas deferens* into the *seminal vesicles* which serve as storage tubes. During sexual excitement, fluids from the prostate and the seminal vesicles serve to float the spermatozoa along and arouse in them their intense latent activity. At the time of ejaculation the seminal discharge, of about a teaspoonful or more, containing many millions of these microscopic cells, is forced out through the urethra. Any healthy one of them, if it reaches a ripe egg cell in the Fallopian tube of the woman, is sufficient to cause pregnancy.

At certain more or less regular intervals the seminal vesicles and the prostate gland become filled with seminal fluids and the internal pressure produces sufficient sexual feeling to cause the expulsion of the contents through the penis in what is called a *seminal emission*. In most unmarried men who do not indulge in sexual relations or produce the sexual orgasm by means of self release (masturbation) this normal process may occur during sleep every few weeks. This discharge is sometimes accompanied by vivid dreams of sexual experience but may take place without the man being aware of any particular feeling or idea. After marriage and the establishment of more or less regular sexual habits these emissions seldom appear except during long periods of sexual abstinence.

HORMONES

It is now a well established fact that both the testicles and the ovaries have a double function in the lives of men and women. While the testicles and ovaries have a special function in the process of reproduction, they also regularly give off into the system certain chemical exciters called *hormones*, which make for general good health and which help the

system to maintain its manly or womanly characteristics.

In some quarters the idea prevails that one needs
to have regular sexual relations in order to keep the
organs in healthy condition. Practical experience and
scientific observation fail to support this opinion,
however, for as a matter of fact the glands are never
wholly idle. Their steady function of producing hormones, a process of which the individual remains
wholly unconscious, is sufficient to keep them in
proper condition so that when called upon for full
sexual service they are ready for action. Like the
tear glands, the reproductory organs will function
after years of apparent disuse, provided the rest of
the body is healthy and the glands have not been
otherwise diseased.

REFERENCES

Dickinson, R. L., *Atlas of Human Sex Anatomy,* Williams and Wil-
    kins, Baltimore, 1933.

Lewis, W. H., *Gray's Anatomy of the Human Body,* Lea & Febiger,
    Phila., 1930, 22d Ed., pp. 1227-1260.

Murrell, C. M., *Health and Empire,* Vol. V, No. 4, Dec., 1930, Lon-
    don, "Normal Adolescence in Girls," pp. 317-318.

Novak, Emil, *The Woman Asks the Doctor,* Williams and Wilkins,
    1935.

Parshley, H. M., *The Science of Human Reproduction,* Norton, N. Y.,
    1933, Chap. IV, "Hormones."

CHAPTER IV

PLANNING THE HONEYMOON

The intimate experiences of the first few weeks of married life are usually such that they stand out in memory and exert a greater influence for good or for evil than any other similar period in life. Honeymoons may be delightful or tragic, according to the intelligence and good judgment used in planning for them.

Regardless of where the newlyweds go or what they do, the most significant events of this period are likely to be their first ventures into full sexual intimacies. This being the case, it is well to consider under what circumstances the average couple is likely to have the most satisfying experiences.

TRAVEL

Just why people should insist on a trip to start their honeymoon is more than reason can determine. It may be the old wish to escape the bantering of relatives and friends and thus secure some measure of privacy, or it may be the desire to find some romantic spot in which to commence their marriage relationship. At all events, it has become a general custom to take a trip and too often this custom is followed blindly, regardless of whether or not it affords the privacy and happiness desired.

As a rule, the first few days are best spent in a quiet place as free from stress and hurry as possible. The last minute rush and the general nervous tension accompanying most weddings do not leave either bride or groom as free from fatigue and worry as they should be to enter upon their new life together. It is enough that two people are required to make numerous personal adjustments during this period without having to visit relatives, hurry to catch trains, fight against seasickness, or to try to be comfortable in an utterly strange situation.

Probably the best arrangement for the average couple is to slip away to some comfortable hotel or house where they can spend the first day or two in quiet relaxation. The possibility of seasickness usually makes boat travel a matter of doubtful wisdom, and unless the couple can afford a drawing room, the average sleeping car is not to be recommended for honeymoon travel. Crowding in upon relatives, especially if sleeping and bath facilities are limited, is also to be avoided in most cases. If the first night must be spent in travel, by all means let the second be passed in some quiet spot where both partners, after a day's relaxation, may be ready to explore the mysteries of sexual love.

FAVORABLE CONDITIONS

The most favorable conditions for a honeymoon and for commencing sexual relations are: (1) quietness, (2) the absence of a definite time schedule, (3) freedom from the intrusion by others, (4) com-

fortable beds and living quarters, and (5) adequate
equipment to guard against pregnancy where this is
to be avoided. If the couple is rested, free from anxiety over other matters, and possessed of the general
information relative to sexual behavior in marriage,
the partners are ready to commence their sexual relationship. Given the proper privacy, it matters little
whether the time be day or night so long as *both* are
free to enter the experience with a happy expectancy.

Comfortable Beds

The importance of the first three items are so
self evident that it seems superfluous to do more
than mention them. The question of beds, however, deserves more attention than it often receives
in making plans for the honeymoon and for the
new home. Comfortable beds are one of the most
important items in any household, and a couple will
be well repaid if they give intelligent attention to
this matter when planning their honeymoon. What
little time there is for sleep is too precious to be
spent in restlessness or discomfort due to poor beds.
Whatever else is sacrificed when finances are limited,
it is not good to economize too much on beds either
on the honeymoon or in furnishing the home.

Many couples prefer to sleep in a double bed. Such
an arrangement is less expensive, requires less room,
less bedding, and less laundry than separate beds.
Those who have been accustomed to sleeping alone
will probably find it a bit difficult to become used to
having another person moving about in bed beside

them, sleepily adjusting covers. It often takes a little time to become a good bedfellow.

The best bed is one that is not too hard, nor yet so soft and flexible that it wiggles and shakes all over when one moves a hand or foot. If one of a couple is accustomed to a very soft and the other a moderately hard bed, or if one needs many covers and the other few, it will be necessary to compromise a little to arrive at a satisfactory arrangement.

Above all a good bed should not squeak. Nothing is more disconcerting than to have a bed squeak with every movement, especially during the process of sexual relations, when there is a possibility that such noise may be overheard.

Some couples prefer twin beds. Such an arrangement has much to commend it, for there are few people who do not sleep better when they sleep alone. Some couples object to them, however, on the grounds that they are "less chummy and companionable." This is largely a matter of taste, for if two beds are in the same room and close together it is possible to converse freely without raising the voice so high that it need be heard outside. Separate bedrooms are seldom necessary or advisable, except in case of illness. Whatever convenience they give in the way of extra closet space and personal privacy may be offset by the undesirable tendency to exclusiveness.

Dressing and Undressing

During the early days of marriage, many couples find it somewhat embarrassing to dress and undress in the same room. This is quite natural, for feelings and habits of many years cannot be discarded without some effort. As a couple becomes more intimately acquainted this slight embarrassment usually wears away and they lose all sense of uneasiness over being seen by each other in partial or complete undress. Here again, each couple should feel free to work out the particular arrangement that will best fit its own needs. There are those to whom the unseen, with its suggestion of mystery, makes a stronger appeal than the seen.

Most men and boys, and many girls, are accustomed to undress in the presence of others of their own sex and are not in the least embarrassed by it. Some girls, on the other hand, have been brought up under a different code and can hardly be expected to cast off their habitual reserve at once. Whether they ever do or not is a matter of individual choice and privilege. Husbands will be gracious in this matter, knowing that in time the increasing familiarities of the home will serve to adjust such matters in a natural and comfortable manner.

Unembarrassed nudity within the privacy of the home has certain very definite values. Children who grow up accustomed to seeing not only their brothers and sisters, but also their parents in the process of dressing and bathing, seldom develop the nasty sex curiosity which haunted the minds of past generations. The ability to distinguish between shame and modesty is a personal achievement that is invaluable.

Bathing

Plans for the honeymoon as well as for the home should include convenient bathing facilities. Perspiration odors and any form of bodily uncleanliness are very offensive to some people. A comfortable bath before retiring removes the possibility of any such offense to one's beloved and gives one the distinct psychological advantage of feeling utterly clean and refreshed from the days' contacts. Then, too, quite apart from the weather, the increased rapidity of circulation during normal sexual intercourse usually causes considerable perspiration, so that a good bath becomes an essential to cleanliness. Where a tub or shower bath is not possible, provision certainly should be made for a good sponge bath in warm water.

CONTRACEPTIVES

No matter how much they desire children, most thoughtful couples will appreciate the importance of having several months, during which they may plan their budget and gain perspective in housekeeping problems in their relation to the care of a family; and during which they may also be wholly free from concern about pregnancy to make the intimate adjustments necessary when persons with different home backgrounds undertake to live together. Habits of eating, sleeping, personal hygiene, tidiness, promptness, and many other forms of behavior often assume totally different aspects when associated with the habits and expectations of one's marriage partner. Thus the average couple needs a few months in which to become fully adjusted, before being called upon to plan for a child.

There are instances where conditions of health, employment, and financial support are such that the coming of a child would be little short of a calamity, but where the couple alone might commence its married life and enjoy the intimacies of wedlock with profit and safety, provided it knows what to do to avoid conception.

Up until quite recently the Federal Postal Laws have forbidden the transportation by the mails, or any common carrier, of any articles or information specifically intended or adapted for contraceptive purposes. [*Davis v. United States, 62 Fed.* (2d) 473 (*Circuit Court of Appeals, 6th Circuit,* 1933) (*Mail and Interstate Commerce*).] More recently the mails have been opened, by court interpretation, to licensed physicians engaged in legitimate medical practice. [*United States v. One Package containing 120, more or less, Rubber Pessaries to Prevent Conception* (*Circuit Court of Appeals, 2d Circuit, Dec.* 7, 1936) (*Importation from a foreign country*).] Even under existing regulations, however, there have been few attempts, and none successful, to prosecute a reputable physician for giving his patients such information.

All that need be said here is that there are now available methods of contraception which are highly reliable and in no wise likely to endanger the health of either husband or wife. For their own peace of mind every couple should know what may properly be done to postpone or space the coming of children without interfering in any way with those sexual intimacies which are an expression of affection between husband and wife.

No present method of contraception, however, whether "natural," medical, or mechanical, is wholly fool-proof and absolutely one hundred per cent reliable.* In a small number of instances conception takes place even when supposedly reliable methods have been employed. If this occurs, and there are no serious health problems involved, it should be accepted calmly as a surprise and not as a calamity. Should the wife miss her usual menstrual period and pregnancy be suspected, she should consult her physician at once to determine, (a) whether she is pregnant or not, (b) whether her health is endangered by this fact if this is the case, and (c) what medical care she should have.

By means of the Aschheim-Zondek test it is possible to determine within a few days' time whether a woman is pregnant or not. The fact that this test may be applied during the first few weeks of pregnancy, before it is usually possible to determine this fact by other methods is a matter of considerable consequence where the health and permanent welfare of the mother is concerned.

* The "rhythm" method is at present receiving much study, but results remain inconclusive.

ABORTION

After conception has taken place and a new life begins to grow, it is a very serious matter, both physically and morally, for anyone to attempt to remove or destroy it. Abortion is legal only when a competent physician determines that the life of the mother would be gravely endangered by the continuance of the pregnancy. It should be undertaken only by a skilled surgeon and in a hospital properly equipped for the purpose. During the past year a large part of the maternal death rate (estimated by some as high as twenty-five per cent) was due to abortions attempted under illegal and unfavorable conditions. For healthy married couples it is almost invariably better to accept the situation cheerfully and make sure that the infant never knows that he was not originally planned for at the time he came. Such an arrangement may postpone educational or other family projects but it seldom need prevent their ultimate accomplishment.*

PRE-MARITAL PHYSICAL EXAMINATION

Not only the problem of contraception, but the general importance of good health and happiness should lead every bride and groom to have a thorough physical examination before setting the date of the wedding. This should include not only a complete physical examination, but special consideration should

* An excellent anonymous article on "The Unwanted Child" appeared in the *Parents Magazine* for November, 1936, p. 116. Couples faced with this perplexity will do well to read it.

be given to the reproductory organs and to whether either party has any communicable disease or infection which might be transmitted to the other or to their offspring.

If the physician, in addition to other common items would check on the following facts for the bride and the groom, an important step toward preventing those barriers to happiness which have disturbed or wrecked so many marriages will have been taken.

The Man's Examination

(1) Has he the normal capacity for sexual erection—is he sexually potent?

(2) Is the penis well developed and free from disease or malformation?

(3) If not circumcised, is the prepuce or foreskin free from all adhesions to the glans and capable of being drawn back so as to fully expose it?

(4) If there has been a history of venereal disease has the proper treatment been given and do the tests show a complete cure?

(5) Are there any psychic conditions which may adversely affect satisfactory sexual performance?

The Woman's Examination

(1) Is the hymen thin and easily stretched or is it very thick and so tough that it needs a

slight incision or dilation before marriage to prevent excessive pain at first intercourse?

(2) Is the vaginal cavity well developed and within the usual range of depth and width?

(3) Is the uterus well developed and in proper position?

(4) Is the clitoris visible and free from adhesions to the prepuce which covers it?

(5) Does she have any communicable disease?

(6) Are there any general health conditions which might make pregnancy and childbirth dangerous to the woman's health?

(7) If contraception is indicated, what method will be most suitable?

(8) Are there any psychic conditions which might adversely affect satisfactory sexual performance?

REFERENCES

Bromley, Dorothy Dunbar, *Birth Control, Its Uses and Misuse*, Harpers, New York, 1934.

Dickinson, R. L., "Premarital Examinations," reprint from *American Journal Obstetrics and Gynecology*, November, 1928.

Dickinson, R. L., and Bryant, Louise S., *The Control of Conception*, Williams and Wilkins, Baltimore, 1932. (Available only on physician's order.)

Groves, E. R. and Gladys H., *Wholesome Marriage*, Houghton Mifflin, New York, 1927, Chap. V.

Hartman, Carl G., *The Time of Ovulation in Women*, Williams and Wilkins, Baltimore, 1936.

Kopp, Marie E., Ph.D., *Birth Control in Practice*, McBride, N. Y., 1934.

Latz, Leo J., *The Rhythm of Sterility and Fertility in Women*, Latz Foundation, Chicago, 1933.

Matsner, Eric M., *The Technique of Contraception*, Williams and Wilkins, Baltimore, 1934. (Available only on physician's order.)

Novak, Emil, *The Woman Asks the Doctor*, Williams and Wilkins, Baltimore, 1935.

Parents Magazine, November, 1936, p. 116. "The Unwanted Child," Anonymous.

Sanger, Margaret, and Stone, Hannah, *The Practice of Contraception*, Williams and Wilkins, Baltimore, 1931. (Available only on physician's order.)

Stone, Abraham and Hannah, *A Marriage Manual*, Simon and Schuster, N. Y., 1935, pp. 102-103.

CHAPTER V

THE TECHNIQUE OF SEXUAL INTERCOURSE

THE NEED FOR INSTRUCTION

It has been widely assumed by many persons that the process by which the sexes unite in the copulatory act is so simple and instinctive in nature that there is no need for giving any instruction concerning it. Others assume that even if the bride is uninstructed, the average man is sufficiently informed so that there is little need for any technical guidance in the art of intercourse.

That both these assumptions are without adequate foundation can readily be illustrated by numerous cases appearing almost daily in the offices of physicians and marriage consultants. One physician reports that within the space of a single year wives of a college professor, a merchant, and a physician came to him for apparent sterility. In each case it developed that these supposedly intelligent people did not have children because they were ignorant of the proper technique of intercourse. After receiving proper instruction two of the three women became pregnant within a few months' time. There are many cases where couples married for one, two, or more years report they have had not a single instance of successful intercourse in all that time.

Nor is this ignorance confined to those without

pre-marital sex experience. The old adage that "practice makes perfect" proves utterly false unless practice takes place under favorable conditions and proceeds along skillful lines. Practice does not help unless it is good practice. Much of the pre-marital sex experience of men and women takes place under the handicap of so many fears, anxieties, and uncertainties, that it is usually little more than a hasty, blundering attempt to express a powerful, instinctive drive. Where some people learn to perform properly by means of pre-marital experimentation, more are very definitely harmed by the unfortunate psychological consequences of such trial and error methods.

One young man desiring experience before marriage sought the companionship of a married woman whose husband was away much of the time. The first time he spent the night with her his inexperience was laughed off in fun. On the second occasion his ineptness was made the butt of considerable ridicule, the woman declaring him "no good" as compared with her husband. The psychic effect of this experience was damaging to the young man's self confidence and resulted in temporary impotence.

A young couple who felt it necessary to postpone marriage for economic reasons, ventured to indulge in sexual relations to relieve their emotional tensions. Neither had any effective information as to procedure, and after some two dozen unsatisfactory occasions, the girl decided she must be sexually inadequate and questioned the advisability of going on into marriage. After physical examination revealed them to be structurally normal the couple were given adequate instruction which made for an easy adjustment in their marriage.

A young clergyman resolved to provide suitable instruction for all his wedding couples and presented each with a good book in the subject of sexual adjustment in marriage. The father of one such bride-to-be met him on the street one day and peremptorily called him into his office. Expecting a reprimand for daring to give the girl and her fiance the book, he was happily surprised to be heartily thanked, not only for giving the book to the couple, but because it had brought information and satisfaction to the girl's parents who were considering separation on the grounds of sexual incompatibility.

Many such illustrations might be added but these are enough to show that a clear understanding of what has been the best experience of the race in these matters can help to make beautiful and endearing what all too often is a sordid and divisive aspect of marriage.

Helpful Attitudes

Any discussion of the techniques of sexual intercourse runs the risk of implying that success is largely a matter of mechanics, of touching this, or patting that, or of some particular position, time, or frequency. The facts are, rather, that any dependence on mechanical procedures must always be secondary to mental and emotional attitudes if success is to be real and lasting. Men and women are not automatons moved by mechanical motors and electric push-buttons, but rather living spirits swayed by feelings and emotions. It is in this latter realm, rather than in dependence on mechanical techniques, that help is most likely to come for those having difficulties.

(1) *Playfulness.* Except when used for specifically reproductive purposes, the sexual act is, in fact, a highly specialized form of play. As such it serves the public good by strengthening the marriage tie and encouraging the seeking of sexual satisfactions within the home rather than outside of it. During play one casts aside all feelings of desperate seriousness and enters into the mood of the occasion, quite willing to play an unusual role for the time in order to find added enjoyment. Within the privacy of the marriage chamber a couple may properly discard most of the external social conventions and conduct themselves as fancy directs, so long as they are in fine sympathy with each other, and do not forget the mutual nature of their goal. Variations in time of day, of place, and position may all enter into this spirit of playfulness. It is necessary to remember only that what may be play to one partner, may not always be play to the other, and what may be play at one time may not so be regarded when one is in a different mood or a different situation. It takes sympathy and understanding to lead or to follow in play which promotes real affection and fellowship.

The spirit of playfulness is of special importance to those who experience unusual difficulties with emotional fixations, frigidity, or other forms of emotional blocking. Where such hindrances exist it is seldom that success can be achieved by any form of intense effort. Seriousness and strained endeavor are often the chief causes of failure. The spirit of carefree playfulness can often accomplish more than any amount of intensity and desperation.

(2) *Gentleness*. Perhaps the finest tribute that a wife can pay to her husband's love is to say, "No one could ask for a gentler man than my husband." Gentleness is always in order and always appreciated.

(3) *Cooperation*. Sexual relations in marriage concern two persons. It is never just a matter of one person seeking his own satisfaction. Since the goal is mutual happiness, the two concerned need ever to keep in mind that each must be considerate of the other in every phase of the process. To study eyes and moods, to whisper encouragement and helpful suggestions, to wait or to speed up for the other's sake, all this is vital in making such intimate experiences strengthen the bonds of fellowship and mutual enjoyment.

(4) *Patience*. The first attempts at sexual relations are not always successful or highly satisfactory to either party. This is true whether one or both partners has had some previous sexual experience with other persons or not. Each couple is a new combination and must work out by experience those adjustments which are particularly suited to their own needs. If the bride is unable to perform just as she might be expected, the husband must be patient and

not find fault or be disappointed in her. If the groom has difficulties, the bride should be equally considerate and patient. In some cases it takes weeks or even months to develop a fully satisfactory technique, but with patience and loving cooperation it is almost invariably possible. Comparatively few couples are physically mismated to the degree that sexual satisfaction is not a practical possibility.

THE FIRST UNION

Whether a couple attempts to engage in sexual relations the first night after their wedding or not, is a matter for each couple to decide for themselves on the basis of their physical and emotional condition and in the light of the total circumstances surrounding their wedding.

Among some ancient and primitive people the first sexual union of bride and groom was to all intents and purposes a part of the wedding ceremony itself. Guests of the family commonly waited outside, and in some cases, within the same house or room until the "signs of virginity" were shown as evidence that the marriage had been duly consummated. Among some tribes the older customs persisted among royalty and the chieftains long after they had been discarded by the common people. In Samoa, public defloration of the chief's daughter at marriage continued until forbidden by the United States Government.

In other lands and ages the actual coming together of brides and grooms have been deliberately postponed for one, two, or sometimes many nights. It is clear therefore that there neither is, nor has been, any uniform practice in this matter, and it may well be assumed that in the long run it has little to do with success or happiness in marriage. Reasons were to be found for each of these customs in the social life of the day. We ought to be free to adapt this aspect of life to our particular and personal needs, and not feel bound to a slavish observance of any meaningless and outworn custom.

Most husbands will find no serious difficulty in waiting one night, or several, for love's consummation, especially if this is understood beforehand, and the couple realize the advantage of being physically and emotionally at their best when they enter into it. Probably the wife should have chief consideration in this matter for she usually has the more difficult adjustment to make. The considerate husband will not be too reserved, but neither will he be wholly unmindful of her preferences.

Sometimes it develops that in their attempt to be cautious in this matter, a couple makes plans that are too arbitrary, too mechanical, and do not take into consideration the possibility of changes in circumstances and feeling. The bride who expected to be tired and anxious for sleep may find herself not so tired, and far more eager for caressing and sex-play than she is for slumber. In such cases she should let her husband know how she feels and free him from any obligation to wait.

Again, it may happen, in the absence of any agreement before marriage, that a bride may come to the wedding chamber eager and expectant of the joy of the first sexual embrace. If the husband has assumed that he must not approach her for one or several nights, and she does not know the reason for his aloofness, there is a fair chance that she may be keenly disappointed in him and conclude that she has married a man who is either ignorant, indifferent, or impotent. A previous mutual understanding that whatever agreement they make is subject to adjustment will prove most satisfactory in the end.

THE INVITATION

Occasionally it comes about as a natural consequence of love-play that husband and wife become simultaneously conscious of desire for sexual union. More often, however, one partner or the other first has the wish to proceed to this goal and by some word or act communicates the fact to the other.

As couples come to understand one another more fully certain special forms of behavior will be associated with sexual desire, and the observing partner will be able to interpret these signs of invitation or willingness. Occasionally these invitations may be in verbal form but more often they will consist simply in some special caress, or that intensity of caressing which is an unmistakable sign of sexual ardor. The wife should always be as free as the husband to initiate such proceedings.

A word of caution is in order here. Many brides are, by training, if not by nature, somewhat more shy and modest in the matter of sexual expression

than the average husband. They usually react un-
favorably to coarse and vulgar language and to sexual exhibitionism on the part of the man they love.
The average husband will do well to use the more
subtle and indirect approach rather than the spoken
word or bodily exposure. Thoughtful consideration
for the preferences of the woman in such matters is
likely to be very helpful. This applies particularly to
the invitation and the beginning of the foreplay.

THE RIGHT TO REFUSE

No invitation is a true invitation unless one is as
free to refuse as to accept. Not every sexual invitation in marriage should be answered in the affirma-
tive. There are times when fatigue, illness, or preoccupation with other interests of personal and family life should have precedence over sexual desire.
No couple should allow such invitations to degenerate into demands, nor feel that because the invitation
is refused or postponed that the partner is not sympathetic. A tired wife, or a sleepy, indisposed husband
is seldom in the best mood for such relationships.
The invitation rejected before midnight may be
gladly welcomed at dawn.

A further consideration may well be that some
care be taken not to interpret every desire for caresses as an invitation to complete sexual union. Not
every kiss, not every ardent hug is an expression of
specific sexual passion. Caressing has values of its
own quite apart from any end-object and separate
from being any intentional part of the process of

sexual intercourse. Tender looks, gentle touches, a circling arm, need say no more than, "I love you." It should be left for the special, the more intense, and unusual manifestations of affection to raise the question of specific desire. Unless there is in the minds of a couple some practical distinction between ordinary loving caresses and the more ardent signs of sexual passion, considerable misunderstanding may arise between them at times.

THE SEVERAL PHASES OF COITUS

Each instance of sexual intercourse is a single unit of experience but it is helpful for the beginner to consider the several phases of the experience, so that he may fully appreciate how one step leads on to the next, and these, when properly coordinated, combine to produce a sense of deep satisfaction. The various phases consist of (1) fore-play, (2) entrance, (3) copulative movements, (4) orgasms, and (5) after-play.

The length of time occupied by each phase varies not only with different couples, but on different occasions with the same couple. The important thing is to be able to recognize those signs which indicate when one is ready to pass from one phase to the next.

The Fore-play

Its Purpose. Often the sexual invitation does not come until there has been considerable love-making and the couple become aware of mutual desire. But even after this stage is reached there should be no hurry or sudden impulsiveness about the consummation of the act. The man must understand that his wife may require anywhere from a few moments to an hour of fondling, caressing, and lovemaking before she is as ready for active intercourse as he may be within a few moments. Her sex organs are larger than his, both in size and number and are distributed over a wider area of her body. The inner walls of the vaginal opening need to become sensitive and thoroughly stimulated with sexual feeling before any attempt at entrance is made. Just as it is necessary for the male organ to become stiff and erect before the nerves of sexual feeling become highly sensitive, so the soft external folds and the vaginal passage need to become fully prepared before intercourse can be truly satisfying. Such preparation usually takes longer in a woman than a man unless she comes to the sexual embrace already passionate.

The Wife's Problem: (1) *Relaxation.* Really to enjoy sexual relations the wife must be relaxed and wholly unafraid, not merely willing but glad to enter into the adventure. To bring about this favorable condition it is important that she forget for the time being the restrictions she may have learned concerning personal familiarities, and permit her husband to fondle her freely. His gentle, loving caresses with lips and hands, his warm, strong body pressed close against her, will help prepare her. Lips, breasts, curves and folds become strangely sensitive with such caressing and she will find with a little experience that she needs just this sort of playful love-making to prepare mind and body for the experience of sex communion. Ellis declares: "Every woman has her own system of manifest or latent erogenic zones, and it is the lover's part in courtship to discover these zones and to develop them in order to achieve that tumescence which is naturally and properly the first stage in the process of sexual union." Some women respond to poetry, some to soft lights or certain kinds of music, others to various kinds of sentimental love talk. Let her throw off reserve, and in the refuge of her lover's embrace join in the fondling and caressing which are intended as a preparation for this sacrament of love.

(2) *Lubrication.* The woman is not fully ready for sexual union until there is ample lubricating fluid over and around the inner lips and the vaginal opening, so that the entrance of the male organ will not cause unnecessary friction. Usually, as soon as she is sexually excited, the lubricating glands start working, and within a few moments the necessary moisture is present. Some women have an abundance of this fluid, and others a lesser supply. When it seems that she is otherwise ready, either the wife or the husband may test for proper lubrication by gently running the finger along the crease of the inner folds about the sexual opening. Adequate fore-play will usually result in such necessary lubrication but if, on occasion, the woman is thoroughly aroused and yet the surface is dry, a good lubricating jelly should be applied. (See page 145.) It is better to have too much than too little.

(3) *The Hymen.* When the actual time for making the entrance is at hand, the wife may need to assist or direct the husband in locating and, in case of the first union, getting past the resistance offered by the hymen. The first entrance is not often made by one swift movement, but rather by steady gentle pressure, perhaps several times repeated with plenty of lubrication. If there is any great discomfort in making the entrance, it may be that the hymen is unusually thick and so will not stretch or give way enough to allow the male organ to enter the vagina. If this should be the case, and nothing were done to correct it, weeks and even months might pass before the husband could make entrance. This would put severe strain on both man and woman. When such a tough membrane is encountered, instead of being violent and determined, the husband should arrange for his wife to consult a physician trained in these matters and have his advice and treatment. This is another good reason for two or three days of quiet before starting on a strenuous wedding trip.

The usual remedy in such cases is either a gradual stretching of the membrane by the fingers of wife or husband, or a notching of it under a local anesthetic, which takes but a few moments, and is a very simple matter. It is becoming a common practice to have this matter attended to *before the wedding day,* so that this difficulty need not complicate a couple's first efforts in sex expression. The usual procedure is for the bride to consult her physician on the subject as a part of her pre-marital physical examination. If dilation of the hymen seems advisable, she arranges to have it done some time before the wedding, with the knowledge and consent of the prospective husband.

In the case of some women the hymen is naturally so elastic as to be negligible, and presents no problem.

(4) *The Clitoris.* In most women the chief seat of sexual sensation is the clitoris. For this reason it is essential that the posture and motion of coitus be such as to develop in the clitoris an increasing sense of pleasure which gradually cumulates and finally culminates in the orgasm. Although the husband may be well aware of this general fact he cannot know at any particular time whether his behavior is accomplishing that purpose or not unless his wife informs and directs him. Many women find that after such preliminary love-play as kissing, patting, and stroking various parts of the body they are best made fully ready for coitus by having the husband gently manipulate the clitoris and surrounding folds with his finger. By repeated experimentation the couple will discover just what pressure, rhythm, or combination of touch and stroke will best prepare the way for an easy and complete orgasm.

After the entrance has been made it will be necessary for the wife to make sure that the position and the motions are such that this stimulation of the clitoris will be continued. If the male organ tends to lie too low in the vulvar groove so that it does not press or touch the clitoris in the copulative movements she

may need to help the husband move upward and forward so that the clitoris stimulation is a continuous part of the action. Sometimes a firm pillow under
the woman's hips will change the slope of the pelvis
so that this contact may be more easily maintained.
Occasionally it will be most satisfactorily accomplished by the woman assuming the uppermost position and taking the more active part in the movements. In all events the woman will need to keep in
mind the importance of clitoris stimulation and, if
necessary, guide her husband in securing it.

The Husband's Problems: (1) *Relaxation.* The
best mood for successful participation in sex relations is not a tense, excited, or nervous state, but
one of supple and controlled readiness. A man is
ready for sexual union as soon as his penis is stiff,
firm, and erect. Most men are quickly and easily
ready, but the presence of the erection is not the only
thing to be considered. He needs to have in mind,
not only his own condition, but also that of the
woman. He has more than his own desire to consider. His penis is simply the instrument by which
he seeks to accomplish a desired result both for himself and for his partner. He must learn to control it,
and not be carried away by its tendency toward
automatic and reflex action. It may take time to ac-
quire this sort of control, but with patience it is
possible.

(2) *Premature Ejaculation.* By the time he has
caressed and fondled his wife so that she is ready for
the next stage of intercourse, the husband may find

himself so highly excited that as soon as his penis comes in contact with the female sex parts his orgasm occurs forthwith. Quickly after the man's orgasm occurs erection subsides; the penis becomes limp and flaccid, and he can do little more until the sexual nerves have had a rest and some time to recuperate. This may be a matter of minutes or hours, according to the capacity of the individual. Under such circumstances the wife must be patient and sympathetic, no matter how eager and ready she herself may be at the time. It is most likely to occur early in marriage or just after an absence of some weeks' duration. After the first flush of excitement many men are less sensitive and better able to control the orgasm. If the difficulty continues for some days or weeks, as a regular thing, a skilled physician should be consulted. Most often it is a psychological condition which can be remedied by a change in technique.

(3) *Psychic Impotence.* A slightly different type of problem is encountered by some men when commencing sexual relations. Coming to marriage with some feelings of uncertainty, inferiority, or anxiety about his sexual capacity, a man may find to his dismay that at the important moment of actual sex connection he is unable to maintain the necessary erection for successful penetration, or that soon after the entrance has been made his erection fades without orgasm or ejaculation. This is, of course, a most embarrassing circumstance. Usually it is a condition that can be overcome, but may require the help of a physician or a psychologist skilled in dealing with sexual

problems. Before seeking such help both bride and groom should experiment in various ways to discover, if possible, the moods, conditions, or procedures which help or hinder the man's readiness for sexual activity.

The tradition that a man who has difficulty in performing the sex act is not a successful husband, may account for a tendency toward panic if he does experience difficulty. As a matter of fact, it is no more to his discredit that a man be temporarily impotent than for a bride to be frigid and unresponsive when she first commences sexual activity. Both conditions are largely matters of fear and uncertainty, and can be overcome by careful and intelligent effort. It has no necessary connection with venereal disease or any other infection but is largely a nervous condition resulting from some emotional disturbance.

"The newly married pair," say the Elliotts, "must not be troubled about awkwardness and even lack of success at first; they need to maintain mutual regard and patience in the learning process and even have a certain sense of humor at the lack of skill, as they would in any other area."

Making the Entrance

Signs of Readiness. The average man is ready for intercourse as soon as his sexual organ has become stiff and sufficiently rigid to be pushed into the vagina. The only qualification to this statement is that some men are able to control the ejaculation and orgasm much better if they deliberately wait a while before making the entrance until the first flush of passion has somewhat subsided.

The woman is ready for the entrance when, as suggested on page 95 above, she feels highly stimulated and there is ample lubrication at the inner lips of the vulva, and in and about the vaginal opening. Any attempt to make the entrance before such lubrication is present is likely to prove disagreeable and unsatisfactory.

It is not enough that the woman be passive and acquiescent. Just as it is physically impossible for the man to participate without being sexually aggressive, so too, the woman must be stirred beyond mere consent if she is to secure full satisfaction. She must possess the man as much as he possesses her. She must cooperate eagerly in movement and desire and be prepared at times to take the lead when that proves to be mutually helpful. Until she is in this active and expectant frame of mind she is not ready for intercourse.

Dr. Robert L. Dickinson, in the *American Journal of Obstetrics and Gynecology*, writes:

"A woman of refinement, unless she is swept away by passion, requires or desires certain preliminaries. Her zones are three: the mental, the surface erogenous area, and the vaginal; . . . The mental zone is stimulated by loving words and an atmosphere of tenderness. The second zone calls for the kiss or deep kiss, the breast caress or nipple excitation, and the vulvar contacts. The third, or vaginal zone may not become aroused until she has passed through the two preliminary phases of feeling. It is therefore essential that the man should understand the need for special attention to these zones, and specially to the clitoris and other parts of the vulva, during the early weeks and months, in order that adequate stimulation and complete climax be effected."

Positions for Intercourse

When a couple has passed through the necessary steps of sexual excitation and are ready to make the entrance the problem of the position to be assumed arises. Any position is right, any position is proper which permits full sexual enjoyment for both parties. All parts of the body are equally proper for use, provided they can be made to contribute to the happiness of this relationship and do not offend against the taste or feelings of either partner.

Human beings have to learn how to perform when engaging in sexual relations; they are not instinctively prepared for it. Each couple must find by experimentation which positions best suit their personal tastes and body-build. No one way is best for all people, or under all circumstances.

Among the factors which determine the most satisfactory positions are: the slant and depth of the vagina; the high or low placement of the clitoris on the pelvis, the amount of fatty tissue on and about the hips, the comparative length of the two bodies, the length and slant of the erect penis, the presence or absence of pregnancy, and most important of all, the ability of the woman to experience the orgasm in a given position.

The Husband-above Position. The most common position for intercourse is probably that in which the woman lies on her back with knees flexed and spread apart to give easy access to the vaginal opening. The man lies between her legs, and bending forward above her, supports his weight on one arm. In this position he guides the penis into the vaginal opening with his free hand, being careful to insert it at about a forty-five degree angle downward. After the entrance, the relative position of the two may be shifted so that both may be comfortable. Enough of the man's weight can be borne on his elbow or knee so he will not bear down too heavily on the wife. The couple are now in a position where kisses and caresses and whispered suggestions may be easily exchanged. A little practice will indicate how much freedom the woman needs to move about beneath, in order to make the necessary contacts for her continued stimulation as she progresses toward orgasm.

A variation of this position is that in which after entrance is made as above, the woman straightens one leg, and the man puts one of his outside it, so that the woman's leg comes between his two. This makes it possible for both to lie comfortably with legs extended, the man resting mostly on his side. In some cases it will also give opportunity for a more direct pressure on the connected organs. This position has the advantage of being less tiring when intercourse continues for some time, and gives freedom for considerable movement without the risk of separating the organs.

When, as it occasionally happens, the penis is too

long for the woman's vagina, still another variation in this position is practicable. After making the entrance the woman straightens her legs and the man spreads his so that he is outside both of hers. In this position he is lifted somewhat higher than usual and the penis cannot reach quite so far into the vaginal canal. With some care and experience the proper stimulation of the clitoris can be combined with the proper internal movements without breaking connection or causing the wife any discomfort.

The Wife-above Position. This may be accomplished in either of two ways. Connection may be made as in the husband-above position, after which they roll over so that the woman is on top, care being taken not to separate the united organs. Or, the man lies on his back with legs extended while his wife kneels astride him with her legs spread so as to facilitate the insertion of the penis into the vagina, and then leans forward and straightens her body upon his, or rests her weight mostly upon her arms as she may prefer. This is not only a pleasing variation in sex play, but some women are able to obtain orgasm only in this position. It permits the wife to adjust her position so that she can get the proper pressure on her clitoris against the man's pubic bone, and obtain her orgasm even after he may have been premature with his.

The Side Position. There are two or three of these but they are in fact little more than further adaptations of the face-to-face relationships found in the husband-above and wife-above positions. Perhaps the commonest is that in which the man lies on his left side with his left leg drawn up at a right angle to his body and the wife lies on her right side with the hollow of her waist across the man's thigh. It is possible for her to place her left leg over her husband's right leg and so adjust her hips that the entrance can be readily made. When this has been done she rests upon him very much as in the wife-above position previously described except that her hips still rest upon the bed below the man's drawn up thigh. Not every couple finds this position one which suits their bodily proportions but it is most convenient for others.

The Sedentary Positions. There are two of these: one in which the husband lies on his back and the wife sits upright leaning back against his drawn up knees after inserting the penis into the vagina. This was one of the favored Roman positions and is the most passive of all for the man. The other is where the husband sits upon a low chair or stool, a foot or so in height, and the wife sits on his lap facing him with her legs encircling his hips and resting on the floor behind him. It is seldom effective or satisfying unless the woman can brace herself somewhat with her feet on the floor so as to make those particular movements which will afford her the proper stimulation to produce the orgasm.

Rear Entry Positions. While this position is that commonly used by animals and some primitive peo-

ples it is seldom satisfactory to the average couple
except as a form of sex play or when there is some
unusual condition which makes one of the face-to-
face positions undesirable. Entry from the rear may
be accomplished in several different ways. (1) The
wife may assume the knee-chest position, kneeling
on her knees and resting her elbows on a pillow or
the floor, and the husband kneeling behind her makes
the entry facing her back and encircling her waist
with his arms. Rarely is the penis long enough to
extend far into the vagina because the latter is
flanked at the rear by the fleshy buttocks. If she
squeezes her thighs together after penetration the
organs are less likely to separate. Some women prefer
this position during pregnancy to avoid pressure on
the abdomen. Others who need special finger stimulation for the clitoris, and those intensely stimulated
by fondling the breasts may find this position satisfactory. It is also suitable where the husband's penis
is much too long for the wife's vagina, though this
is not the only method overcoming this difficulty.
The use of a disk of sponge rubber with a hole cut
for the penis will prevent too deep an insertion and
at the same time give the clitoris the pressure it needs
for adequate stimulation.

(2) A second method of rear entry is similar to
the preceding except that the wife lies on her side
and the husband approaches from the rear. This is
usually more restful for both and permits of a more
satisfactory fore-play and after-play because it is not
so tiring.

(3) Another rear-entry position is especially useful when for any reason entrance into the vagina is painful and inadvisable, such as after an operation on the uterus or vagina. Following suitable fore-play the woman lies face downward with her legs close together and the man lying upon her inserts the penis in the groove between the thighs so that it touches and moves along the external folds of the vulva and clitoris. In this position the man can enjoy all the normal sensations and by means of supplementary finger stimulation the woman can usually have her orgasm too. By turning her face to one side the woman is in position to kiss and be kissed and if she enjoys having her husband fondle her breasts or manipulate her clitoris he will be free to do so. This position may not meet the needs of every couple but it is, on occasion, a pleasing variation as well as a means of avoiding needless discomfort.

There are numerous other variations in positions but most of them are little more than modifications of these few fundamental ones. To suggest too many at the start is likely to confuse rather than to help the average couple. Each couple is free to experiment and discover which of them are most satisfactory for persons of their body build and temperament.

Copulative Movements

Important Precautions. When both partners are fully prepared for sexual intercourse, the entrance of the penis into the vagina sets up intensive contact stimulation in both. The nerve connections are such that these intense and pleasurable sensations tend to bring automatic or reflex movements of the hips in both man and woman. It is highly important that this reflexive hip movement be controlled as far as possible. Too violent movements may separate the organs, or, what is more serious, may serve to bring on the man's orgasm and loss of erection before the woman has had time to develop hers.

At the beginning, and until the couple are more skilled in the process, it is best for the man to rest a few moments after inserting his penis the full length in the vagina. In most cases the latter organ is surprisingly flexible, especially when the woman is thoroughly excited, and there need be small concern that the penis will be too long. The considerate lover will, however, make his entrance carefully, to avoid causing his bride any discomfort which may take the edge off her sexual excitement.

Gauging Emotional Progress. After the entrance has been made, and the man has rested until he is sure of his control, an occasional forward and backward movement of the penis in the vagina will help to intensify the stimulation for both. Just how long or how rapid these movements should be, and whether it is best for only one member of the couple to make them is a matter to be learned by experience. If movements by the man tend to bring on his orgasm too soon he must learn to wait and let his wife play the active part. In the husband-above position he can lift himself slightly to his knees and elbows so that she is free to make up-and-down, circular, or sidewise movements in whatever manner best suits her need. In the woman-above position she has even better opportunity to make the most satisfactory movements. Care should always be taken not to separate the organs completely, but to make the movements in such fashion that stimulation is provided in two distinct places with each movement: (1) inside, where the enlarged glans of the penis rubs and presses against the mouth of the uterus and along the vagina, and (2) outside, where the area about the base of the penis makes and breaks its contact with the clitoris and with the lips of the vulva.

Increasing Stimulation. In addition to making the rhythmic movements of the hips, some women learn to have considerable control of the muscle which encircles the vagina about an inch inside the external opening. Ability to control this muscle, squeezing the vagina firmly around the penis, greatly increases the stimulation in both sets of organs. It is usually much less violent than the hip movement and can be as gentle or as vigorous as she wishes to produce the proper effect on her husband and herself. As the orgasm approaches, the rhythmic contraction of the vaginal muscles becomes automatic, and with the clitoris and vagina throbbing with stimulation, it is not difficult to bring on the woman's orgasm with a few swift movements. A word or signal to her husband that she is ready will be his cue to unite with her in the last movement to the climax. If the husband feels his orgasm coming on before she has given the signal, he can let her know and she will learn in time how to increase the vigor and intensity of her movements so as to produce her own climax at the same time or quickly after his.

The Orgasms

For the man the orgasm is that stage in the process of sexual excitement where the delight in the act reaches its greatest intensity, and the internal glands release the supply of seminal fluids and propel them out through the urethra by a series of rhythmic contractions. Under ordinary circumstances his orgasm may be produced in five minutes or less, but he will find it more satisfying to prolong the fore-play leading to it for a considerable period of time. Since simultaneous orgasm is the most satisfactory, it is best for the man to postpone his orgasm, if possible, until just after his wife has started hers. Since the ability to maintain erection after entrance averages only from 3 to 5 minutes, it is important for the woman to have been thoroughly aroused before the penis is inserted. Following the orgasm the penis quickly relaxes, becomes soft and loses most of its sexual sensitiveness.

For the woman the orgasm produces no ejaculation of fluid, but is the climax of a series of thrilling and ecstatic sensations in the vagina, and the clitoris, and is accompanied by a series of quick, gasping breaths. This series of spasmodic throbs lasts about ten seconds or less, and then dies away, leaving her relaxed and spent. In some women more than one orgasm is possible, and even necessary, to discharge her battery of desire.

Should this prove to be the regular pattern of the woman's sexual performance then the husband will need to use one of three possible means to satisfy her. (1) He may, if he is able, postpone his own orgasm until she is ready for her second or third and then finish his own simultaneously with her. (2) If she has been thoroughly aroused the husband may continue clitoris stimulation until she has her orgasm and is completely satisfied. (3) He may rest a while and then proceed in the usual manner if time and his own sexual capacity permit.

The After-play

Just as a couple finds peculiar delight in the fore-play which leads to orgasm, so they may also find pleasure and benefit in the after-play which follows it. Instead of drawing apart they should continue the embrace without separating the organs, shifting only so as to lie with both heads in a comfortable position. If they can drift off to sleep in this position so much the better. The sense of unity and mutual love which envelops them as the pleasures of the orgasm slowly fade may be as beautiful and as memorable as a lovely sunset. To drift peacefully into slumber, held closely in the arms of one's beloved is one of the crowning joys of married fellowship.

REFERENCES

Dickinson, Robert L., *American Journal of Gynecology and Obstetrics*, "Pre-Marital Examination as Routine Preventive Gynecology," 1928, p. 631.

Dickinson, R. L., *Atlas of Human Sex Anatomy*, Williams and Wilkins, Baltimore.

Elliott, Harrison Sackett, and Loucks, Grace, *Solving Personal Problems*, Henry Holt, 1936, pp. 104-165.

Ellis, Havelock, *Psychology of Sex*, Emerson Books, p. 30.

Hutton, Isabel Emslie, M.D., *The Sex Technique in Marriage*, Emerson Books, N. Y., 1934, p. 99 ff.

Sumner, W. G., *Folkways*, Ginn and Co., Boston, 1906, pp. 399, 406.

Van de Velde, Th., M.D., *Ideal Marriage*, Covici-Friede, N. Y., 1930, pp. 145-146.

Westermarck, Edward, *Short History of Marriage*, Macmillan, N. Y., pp. 219-223, Tobias Nights.

CHAPTER VI

THE FREQUENCY OF INTERCOURSE

THE PROBLEM OF FREQUENCY

The frequency with which husband and wife may properly engage in sexual relations is a subject of considerable anxiety on the part of many couples. Some who are well adjusted and get a great sense of satisfaction from them, at times wonder whether they are not too self indulgent and tend to develop a guilt complex. Others who fail to find in these intimate experiences the satisfactions they had hoped, question whether the factor of frequency may not have something to do with their disappointment.

In general it may be said that where a couple secures a high degree of emotional satisfaction on most occasions, the question of frequency is of rather small importance. It is the quality of the experience rather than its frequency that is the largest factor in determining its value. While it is possible to indulge too frequently, that danger is relatively small where both partners are considerate of one another and each gets a full measure of satisfaction out of such relationships.

"Satisfied people," says Harris, "do not overvalue sex. Being satisfied, they crave no outside sexual excitement. Having learned how to gain full satisfaction, they are safe to approach each other purely in response to their real desires. They need not worry about how many times per month. If every episode of sexual relations satisfies them both, they are highly unlikely to overdo the business. If their meetings are unsatisfactory they are very likely to continue restlessly trying to gain satisfaction, to the loss of both health and peace of mind. Those men and women who know how to share the experience from beginning to end, are usually free from the disturbances that create so much turbulence in human beings, and issue in a variety of actions unserviceable to themselves and to society. For them, sex has its intense and significant meanings at appropriate seasons; for the rest, they move about their daily tasks free from its disabling distractions."

MOTIVES FOR INTERCOURSE

In practical life there are three motives for engaging in sexual intercourse in marriage: (a) the conception of a child, (b) the expression of mutual affection, and (c) the releasing of sexual tensions. Often, more than one of these motives is involved in a single instance of intercourse but each deserves a separate discussion.

The Conception of a Child

Biologically, the chief goal of sexual intercourse is the conception of offspring. This objective, and the various problems relating to it will be considered more fully in a subsequent chapter dealing with children. Here it is sufficient to say that for most married couples something more than biology is at stake. The personal and the spiritual values associated with this intimate function of married living extend far beyond the mechanics of fertilization.

Expressing Mutual Affection

In the well-adjusted, happy marriage, most occasions of sexual intimacy will be motivated largely by a mutual desire to express through physical channels the love each feels for the other. Just as one gladly accepts kisses from a loving partner, so one responds with a similar readiness to the caressing which leads to the full sexual embrace, provided the circumstances and the occasion be appropriate. When the couple learns how to secure for both partners the satisfying release which should follow the orgasm, their bodily union comes to symbolize for them that spiritual fellowship which is life's greatest joy.

In view of this fact, sexual union should not be allowed to degenerate into a casual indulgence to be undertaken anywhere, at any time, and disposed of in a hurried fashion. Regard should be had for the proper setting and adequate preliminaries, and also, there should be time for subsequent relaxation. If sexual union is to become and remain a high symbol of mutual affection, it should be reserved for times and circumstances that allow for completeness of ritual. Only so can the couple hope to derive the full benefit of this relationship.

Releasing Sexual Tensions

Many couples find after some months of marriage that one partner has an organic rhythm of sexual desire which exceeds that of the other. It is a constitutional and not necessarily an artificial condition brought on by choice or careless mental attitudes. The wife whose husband's glandular activity is somewhat above her own will, in most cases, find no great difficulty in accommodating him, provided she is able to have an orgasm on most such occasions. Sexual emotions make a rather heavy demand on the nervous vitality of the human body, and most couples will find that some flexible plan of moderation is better than an attempt to gratify every sexual impulse that arises. When either begins to feel the burden of accommodation it is a sign that over-indulgence has already begun and it is time to arrive at a mutual understanding of the limits which should be imposed.

"Whatever the regime may be," says Exner, "that will ultimately prove to be the best adapted to the needs and desires of both partners, moderation is desirable in the early weeks, or until the wife's capacities and inclinations have been developed and revealed. This may require the self-curbing on the part of the husband but it is important. A frequency that may later prove to be quite acceptable and desired on the part of the wife, may be objectionable to her during the awakening developing period. Frank, open confidences between the lovers on these matters, and mutual considerateness is the key."

"Not a few men fall into the notion that every manifestation of sexual impulse that arises spontaneously, must be, or has the right to be gratified, to say nothing of those who deliberately tease their lightly slumbering responses in order to make occasion for indulgence. Must every erection occurring at night, for example, be made the occasion for waking the wife out of a sound sleep one or more times for coitus? Human nature has its limits and the limit is most certain to be reached here. . . . Men should know that erections occurring spontaneously at night are mostly due to reflex stimulation from a full bladder and not from glandular sex tension. Empty the bladder and the need is met."

Some wives have glandular needs which exceed those of the husband, and during times of special excitability the husband may be called upon for more sexual activity than he would choose of his own volition. While such accommodation may be gladly given as an evidence of affection it is a bit different from those occasions when the desire for intercourse is strictly mutual. On such an occasion the husband, or in the reverse situation, the wife, must be as spontaneous as possible and play the part of the good lover.

THE RANGE OF FREQUENCY

During the last few years studies by Pearl, Davis, Dickinson and Kopp have recorded the sexual habits of married couples in America. Their findings have been surprisingly uniform, and since they cover several thousand marriages over a considerable number of years it would appear that they are significant. They show a variation in frequency all the way from those whom Pearl calls, "sexual athletes," indulging regularly once or more a day, to others who indulge only once or twice a year.

Probably the most helpful indication of what might be a reasonable degree of frequency for ordinary couples is to indicate the range within which most couples are included. This shows that for couples between twenty and forty years of age the average is about twelve times a month, or once every second or third day. This average includes some who regularly run as high as once a day or oftener, and others who indulge not more than once a week. A check on the degree of frequency in happy and unhappy marriages shows little difference between the two, leading to the conclusion that frequency, in itself, is of no particular significance one way or the other.

Some couples, where the wife has rather distinct periods of sexual desire, prefer to have several occasions within a few days during a period of natural interest, and then an interval of rest until the next such period. It is seldom wise to build up any sort of a mathematical regularity or definite expectancy lest sexual intercourse degenerate into an unromantic and habitual procedure devoid of all the elements of play and pleasant surprise.

In her study of a thousand married women, Davis found that thirty-five per cent stated that their frequency of desire equaled or surpassed that of their husbands', and about sixty-five per cent that their husbands' exceeded their own.

If the activity of one partner's glands is such that desire appears with a high degree of frequency, as compared with the other's frequency of desire, some sympathetic understanding must be reached, or each partner is apt to consider the other unreasonable.

MUTUAL ADJUSTMENT

Whatever plan a couple agrees upon regarding frequency should be a mutual plan. Neither partner has any rights in the matter that are above the will and pleasure of the other. Any such idea of sexual privileges is intolerable in this day of marriages based upon affection. On the other hand, it should be assumed from the very first that for healthy people sexual cooperation and mutual gratification is an accepted part of the marriage relation.

Any practical system of frequency should fix some sort of maximum, beyond which neither partner will easily entice the other by thoughtless behavior. Where work schedules must be met and grueling tasks faced in office, shop, or home, it is possible at times to overindulge. Where illness or definitely limited strength enters into the situation, further caution must be exercised. In such cases the right to hint or ask and be gracefully denied may be the best sort of loving understanding.

Any agreement as to frequency of sexual practice ought to take into account the rhythm of desire, if such is apparent. Some women are clearly aware of such a rhythm, while others, equally healthy and happy, seem to be unaware of any such period and are as ready and willing for intercourse at one time as another. If a husband or wife does have such definite periods it would seem wise to take these into consideration. In Davis' study, as in certain others, it appears that for many women there is a period of natural glandular stimulation and sex consciousness during the days just preceding and just following the menstrual period. Other things being equal, it would seem advisable to take recognition of these natural crests of desire.

A final requirement of a helpful schedule of sexual relations is that it should not wholly break down the capacity of either husband or wife to remain continent and undisturbed during such periods of necessary sexual limitation as may be caused by illness, absence from one another, pregnancy, or a lengthy period of mental or physical stress. To be so driven by habit that one comes to feel he or she must find some sexual release with another, regardless of personal or social consequences, would be unfortunate indeed. The occasional practice of abstinence, if it has no other virtue, helps to make the renewal of such relations all the more agreeable.

No system of any sort will be automatic and self-enforcing. It takes character, self-control, and patience to build up and maintain the habits and attitudes which make for happiness in marriage. Over-indulgence often exacts a heavy toll. Sometimes it manifests itself in a persistent weariness, lack of enthusiasm, low resistance to colds, or inroads of disease, or, it may so dull the nerves controlling the organs of sex that they refuse to function normally until they have had a good rest.

Some men and women have unnecessary trouble in holding to a system, for spacing their indulgences in sexual relations, chiefly because they do not know how to avoid needless artificial stimulation. Sleeping together regularly and any other form of intimate contact may have such an effect. In such cases, separate beds and a sensible and affectionate reserve may prove helpful in making a happier adjustment.

Hobbies, and some sort of special avocation, are useful for married people as well as for engaged couples who are troubled with excess stimulation. The desire for, and the pleasure in, one another's company can be turned to such a wide variety of profitable and interesting activities, that it is quite unnecessary for any couple to become one-sided on matters of sex. An active interest in music, poetry, athletics, theatricals, social service, handicrafts, church work, or children, illustrates some of the thousand-and-one activities in which a couple may share one another's company and love, and yet not be constantly plagued by sexual desire.

SEXUAL FREQUENCY IN LATER LIFE

Ordinarily as individuals swing on between fifty and seventy all the bodily activities tend to slow up. Teeth, eyes, ears, legs, circulation, and digestion slow down or wear out at different periods and at uneven intervals. In some persons sexual capacities show an early decline while in others sexual vigor continues well on through the sixties and seventies, particularly with those who retain their general good health. While women lose their ability to have children somewhere between forty and fifty years of age, it does not follow that they lose their enjoyment of sexual relations at that time. Not infrequently the release from anxiety over the chance occurrence of undesired pregnancy enables them to enter these experiences with a gladness and freedom not possible before. It is at this period in life that some wives commence to equal or to exceed their husbands in the frequency and the intensity of their desire.

If it happens that the man has already begun his natural decline in sexual vigor, the situation may develop ground for considerable personal disagreement between the two. After forty, it is particularly important that sexual relations be well balanced with conditions of general health and an effort made to keep on the safe side of the line rather than to waste energy and risk fatigue through excessive indulgence. If a couple has wisely increased the store of other common interests the partners will find that sexual intimacies may safely be reduced in number without in any way handicapping expressions of mutual interest and affection. New resources of common interest should be built up to take the place of the naturally declining sex life.

Normally, sex intercourse is a healthy and wholesome function of the human system and may be engaged in by the average couple without noticeable impairment of body or mind. The old analogies which attempted to compare the sexual habits of men and animals are false and misleading. The more constant glandular functions and the element of affection which undergirds the whole family structure amply justify its more frequent employment among human pairs. When wholesomely blended with the other interests of social life, a reasonable use of sexual intercourse makes a steady contribution to family happiness.

"This emotional characteristic of sex interest, when under discipline," says Dr. Sheldon, "renders available the whole energy resources of a personality as a sort of vast reservoir for warming and enriching and supporting character. When out of discipline it can for the same reason devastate a personality almost as effectively and as quickly as can pain or hunger."

REFERENCES

Davis, Katherine B., *Sex Factors in the Lives of 2200 Women*, Harpers, N. Y., 1929.

Davis, Katherine B., *op. cit.*, p 75.

Dickinson, Robert L., and Beam, Lura, *One Thousand Marriages*, Williams and Wilkins, Baltimore, 1931.

Dickinson and Beam, *op. cit.*, p. 143 ff.

Exner, Max J., M.D., *The Sexual Side of Marriage*, Norton, N. Y., 1932, pp. 215-216, 228-229.

Harris, Frederic, *Essays on Marriage*, Association Press, N. Y., 1931, pp. 130-131.

Kopp, Marie C., *Birth Control in Practice*, McBride, N. Y., 1934.

Pearl, Raymond, *The Biology of Population Growth*, Knopf, N. Y., 1925.

Pearl, Raymond, *op. cit.*, pp. 186-197.

Pearl, Raymond, *op. cit.*, pp. 193-202.

Sheldon, W. H., M.D., *Psychology and the Promethean Will*, Harpers, N. Y., 1936, p. 112.

CHAPTER VII

CHILDREN

EARLY AGREEMENTS

One of the things upon which every couple should agree before marriage is children: those conditions under which children would be desirable, and, if so, about how many they would consider an ideal family. The engaged couple that is not sufficiently acquainted frankly to discuss such matters may well question whether they are sufficiently acquainted to get married.

The majority of couples will desire children and be the happier for parenthood. How many children they should plan to have is a matter that should be left somewhat flexible, but an approximation avoids the possibility of irreconcilable differences of opinion later on. The mother's health, the economic status of the family, and the general congeniality of the home life will enter into the final decision. The "right to be well-born" should carry with it the right to a good home, proper education, and suitable parental guidance.

EUGENIC CONSIDERATIONS

Eugenists and population experts declare that it takes an average of nearly four children to a couple to perpetuate the race—two to replace the parents, and one or two to replace those lost by accident or disease. Those who are financially and otherwise able to have large families will find themselves more than repaid for meeting their social obligations by the joys which cluster around the happy family circle.

There are some couples who should marry and purposely avoid having children. Certain types of hereditary diseases should not be passed on to children. Precisely which these diseases are is a matter which any couple having a malady of any sort should investigate before marriage for the sake of a clear understanding as to their right to parenthood.

Other persons with fairly good physical inheritance but with limited strength and ability, due to the contraction of certain non-hereditary diseases, or to some accident, should not plan to have children. Their children might be normal but if either parent is personally handicapped so as to be unable to give them proper care, it would be unfair to the children. Women with epilepsy, mental defects, and certain types of severe neuroses may give birth to healthy children, but their ability properly to care for them is so limited as to make parenthood unwise. Where this question arises a couple should take its problem to a physician for expert advice.

The time at which a couple plan to have their children, as well as how many, is a matter that deserves careful consideration before marriage. Where the choice is between early marriage, involving the postponement of children until some educational or economic responsibility has been met, and later marriage, involving a long engagement period filled with uncertainties and emotional tensions, many couples nowadays choose the former. As far as children are concerned this arrangement works out successfully in some cases, while in others it ends in postponing the event until some unexpected circumstance, or age itself, makes children impossible. Such delay is unfortunate for those who truly desire children. Where the chief hindrance is economic such delays are not always justified.

PLANNING FOR A CHILD

When a couple is ready for a child the first step is to make sure of the physical condition of the wife. Examination by a competent physician, preferably one who specializes in work with women, should be arranged so as to make sure she is physically fit for the undertaking. Some hindrances are temporary in nature and others may require longer treatment. It is wiser to know in advance what to expect than to plunge blindly ahead into pregnancy, perhaps then to find some difficulty that could easily have been remedied beforehand, but which, with the complication of pregnancy, becomes a serious problem. Women with serious physical limitations have been enabled to become happy mothers when they took a capable physician into their confidence *before* pregnancy, and permitted him to guide them from the first in taking precautions to lessen the risks for mother and child.

Having visited the physician and established the

suitable condition of the mother, the next step is to choose the approximate time of the year the couple would prefer to have the child born. Often this makes little difference, but in some climates extreme summer heat, winter cold, or other conditions make a specific period most desirable. Since birth takes place approximately ten lunar months (280 days) from conception, suitable allowance should be made on this basis.

Not every woman becomes pregnant at the first opportunity, some only at widely spaced intervals, and others appear to be permanently sterile. The average couple takes from 3 to 6 months to effect a pregnancy. So far as the monthy cycle is concerned, somewhere between the tenth and the fifteenth day after the *onset* of menstruation appears to be the period during which the average woman is most likely to conceive. Individual women, however, appear to differ widely in this respect. If conception does not occur within a year it is well to consult a physician and have his suggestion as to what may be done to help bring it about.

HINDRANCES TO PREGNANCY

A considerable number of married women find that they do not become pregnant in spite of the fact that they very much desire to have children. Medical studies have shown that the fault is not always with the woman; that often the difficulty is but temporary in nature, and that frequently it responds to treatments which are neither difficult nor expensive. The couple that truly desires children should not accept as final any failure to have children within a year or two but should make every reasonable effort to remove any hindrances to pregnancy.

Among the more common of these are: (1) Inflammation of the lining of the cervix, (2) the closure of the Fallopian tubes, (3) the sterility of the husband, and (4) intercourse at unfavorable times. When the lining of the cervix is inflamed the mouth of the uterus may be effectively closed against the entrance of the sperm cells or the discharge from such an inflamed area may prove fatal to them. Similarly there are sometimes organic and structural conditions which completely close the tubes leading from the uterus to the ovaries so that the sperm and the ovum cannot meet. Various ways have been found to treat each of these conditions so that in a comparatively short while the woman may become pregnant. In about one-third of all cases sterility is due to some inadequacy of the husband. His testicles may have been closed off by a severe case of mumps, or by some injury or disease, or his general vitality may be so low that the spermatozoa lack sufficient vigor to produce conception. Adequate rest, with proper nourishment and medical treatment often are able to correct a certain number of such cases. Because the ovum is available for fertilization for only a day or less during the monthly cycle it is important in some cases of apparent sterility that couples confine most of their sexual relations to the mid-month period, from the tenth to the fifteenth days of the menstrual month being considered the most favorable time. If the man and woman are both known to have been fertile, and no other hindrance seems apparent, the physician is often able to guide a couple in their experimentation until they discover the time of ovulation and are thus able to secure the desired pregnancy. By refraining from sexual intercourse for most of the month and confining their coming together to certain specific days in the cycle it may sometimes be accomplished without any medical aid.

PREGNANCY

Signs of Pregnancy

The absence of menstruation at the usual time, a peculiar tenderness of the breasts, and nausea, particularly in the morning, are some of the common signs by which a woman may know she has become pregnant. In some cases pregnancy may exist where any or all of these conditions are temporarily absent. A laboratory test has been developed whereby it is possible to diagnose a pregnancy when the woman's period is 1 to 2 weeks overdue. Serious problems of health, unexpected necessity of travel into distant regions, and certain other conditions may make it very important that a pregnancy be recognized before the usual signs are evident. The Aschheim-Zondek Test for pregnancy consists of the injection of a small quantity of the woman's urine into an immature female mouse or rabbit. If the pituitary hormones of pregnancy are present in the urine they cause rapid development of the sexual organs of the animals. One to four days after injection, an examination of the animal's ovaries will show maturing ovaries if the woman is pregnant.

Ordinarily, if the couple is anxious to have a child, it is a simple matter of continuing sexual relations and letting conception take place when it will. If the wife misses a second period and is otherwise in good health, the probabilities that she is pregnant are very strong. She should visit her physician at once, and arrange to see him as often as he advises until the child is born. The sooner she puts herself in the care of a good physician the less the danger of complications; and too, if any corrective measures are needed, the earlier they are undertaken the better.

Miscarriage

This is the common term for an interrupted pregnancy. Bleeding from the uterus, and sometimes abdominal pain, are the warning signs that something is wrong. The woman should lie down and call a physician at once, so that the bleeding may be stopped if possible before the embryo is dislodged and expelled.

Such an accident is most likely to occur during the first three months of pregnancy, and particularly at the time when the second and third menstruation would have been in progress were she not pregnant. It is well, therefore, to avoid strenuous exercise at these dates, and also to refrain from sexual intercourse, in order that all possible risk of a disturbance may be avoided.

Sexual Intercourse During Pregnancy

Physicians quite generally agree that there is little harm in continuing sexual intercourse during the greater part of pregnancy *provided* the woman is in good health and desires it. Some women who are rather passive in sexual matters during ordinary times become unusually fond of coitus during pregnancy. If, however, the wife is ill and uncomfortable, intercourse may be very unjust to her and should not be attempted. In all events, the woman's wishes should have first consideration. During the last two months the couple should abstain entirely for the protection of mother and child.

The husband's concern for the welfare of his wife and child will go a long way towards helping him maintain sexual self-control during this period. If he will put any inconvenience of his beside the extra burden his wife is bearing, he will not be seriously tempted to seek sexual satisfaction elsewhere. During the months when intercourse is inadvisable because of pregnancy, the husband will find that his sexual desire may be considerably reduced by sleeping in a separate bed, and avoiding as far as possible all artificial stimulation.

Intercourse After Childbirth

Under usual conditions the woman's pelvic organs return to their normal state by the end of six weeks following childbirth. If her physician does not advise her how soon sexual intercourse may be permitted he should be specifically asked.

CHILDREN IN THE HOME

With the advent of the baby into the home, the usual household routine undergoes something of a change to accommodate the new arrival. In their concern for the welfare of the baby, the family is likely to lose their sense of balance as to what constitutes a well-rounded program of family life. Meal and work schedules are likely to be upset and social obligations ignored. To a certain extent this may be a necessity but it should not be allowed to become permanent.

The mother should not use too much of her limited strength during the first months in an effort to care for both the baby and the household. Home routine that has been simple for the woman before the baby came may become a burden when the care of the little one is added. Children are not a disease, nevertheless a sensible program of convalescence covering at least six weeks following birth would make for the better health of the mother. This is not an unreasonable suggestion when one considers the strain and stress to which the reproductive organs have been subjected. So much of a woman's nervous system is connected with her reproductive organs that when these are not in good condition she cannot be at her best either as mother or wife.

Aside from intelligent care and feeding, the young child needs nothing so much as quiet and sleep, dot-ing relatives and friends notwithstanding. The parents who insist on sparing the child the nervous strain of being exhibited, whether he be a day, a year, or six years old, have abundant support in modern teaching.

An older child can be prepared for the new baby's arrival, so that the newcomer will be anticipated and eagerly welcomed. For such an older child to love and do things for "our baby," and at the same time not feel that he is being neglected, lays the foundation for later comradeship, and avoids building jealousy situations.

Inasmuch as the father is equally responsible with the mother for the life of the child he should be equally concerned with its well-being and training, and will find many ways to assist in its care. When care and discipline are left wholly to the mother, the father tends to become something of an outsider and the fellowship of husband and wife may be endangered by the mother's preoccupation with the child. It largely depends on the parents whether the family circle shall be a happy companionship of all the members or a battle ground of ideas and divided loyalties.

The atmosphere of the home in which a child grows up is more important, often, than the particular type of training he receives. Thom in his "Every day Problems of the Everyday Child" says:

"Conforming to rules and regulations, obeying customs and traditions, being well mannered and properly groomed, all contribute to what we call adjustment to life; but one may be very unhappy and inefficient if, while acquiring these habits of conformity, he fails to develop a broader view of life, which embraces happiness, peace, contentment, love, sympathy, and the finer sentiments. These attitudes are absorbed by the child from the atmosphere in which he lives, and are not acquired through training."

In their love and concern for the child, parents often insist on doing his thinking and choosing for him. They refuse to allow him to grow up, to think for himself and stand on his own feet. To be a successful adult one must be free to develop according to the personality and mental characteristics which he has inherited from past generations, and not be compelled to fit into a pattern fixed by parental ambition.

A Syrian poet, Kahlil Gibran, wrote most aptly to parents:

"Your children are not your children.
They are the sons and daughters of Life's longing for
    itself.
They come through you, but are not from you.
And though they are with you they belong not to you.
You give them your love but not your thoughts,
For they have their own thoughts.
You may house their bodies, but not their souls;
For their souls dwell in the house of tomorrow
Which you cannot visit, even in your dreams.
You may strive to like them,
But seek not to make them like you.
For life goes not backward, nor tarries with yesterday."

Inasmuch as we deal here with the specific problems of sexual adjustments in marriage it is not amiss to call attention to the important fact that adult attitudes are built largely upon the information and understanding obtained in childhood and youth. It is of utmost importance that children be given correct information and attitudes both by word of mouth and by the behavior of parents in the intimate circle of family life. Frank answers to questions and an honest facing of life's facts in a sympathetic, understanding spirit will build a confidence and companionship which will be invaluable to both parents and children.

Sex training, like all learning, begins in the nursery, but there is danger in a child being exposed to experiences which are so far beyond his comprehension that he will be confused and troubled by them. Children see and hear much more than some parents realize and not infrequently, guidance clinics report cases of jealousy, fear, and suspicion resulting from children observing their parents in the act of sexual intercourse. For this reason, it is generally agreed that from eighteen months on, a child should not sleep in the room with his parents. For reasons of health, as well as in the interests of correct habits and behavior, children should have separate beds, even if they must share the same room.

It should not be assumed that because a child is young he should be taught nothing about sex. In a gradual manner he can be given the proper names and functions of the bodily organs of both sexes so that by the time he has reached adolescence he has acquired understanding and poise and is untroubled by incorrect and conflicting information about necessary and wholesome life processes.

From the wealth of child guidance material available today every parent may secure abundant help in seeking to understand his child and to guide him into successful adjustments through adolescence and into adult life. To fail him in this, is to leave him stranded on life's sea or tied to a parental apron string and incapable of living life to the full in the place where he finds it.

REFERENCES

Blanton, Smiley and Margerite G., *Child Guidance*, Century, N. Y., 1927, p. 72.

Blatz, William, and Bott, Helen, *Parents and the Pre-School Child*, Morrow, N. Y., 1929, p. 80.

Broadhead, Geo. L., *Approaching Motherhood*, Hoeber, N. Y., 1930.

Buschke, A., and Jacobsohn, F., *Sex Habits*, Emerson Books, Inc., N. Y., 1933, Chap. X.

Carey, W. H., and Hotchkiss, Robert, *Journal of American Medicine*, Feb. 24, 1934, pp. 587-590, "Semen Appraisal."

Dublin, Louis I., *Population Problems*, Houghton Mifflin, N. Y., 1926, p. 10 ff.

Gibran, Kahlil, *The Prophet*, Alfred A. Knopf, N. Y., 1935, p. 18.

Hartman, Carl G., *Time of Ovulation in Women*, Williams and Wilkins, Baltimore, 1936.

Heaton, Claude E., *Modern Motherhood*, Farrar & Rinehart, N. Y., 1935.

Irving, Frederick C., *The Expectant Mother's Handbook*, Riverside Press, N. Y., 1932.

Langdon, Grace, *Home Guidance of Young Children*, John Day, N. Y., 1931, pp. 26-27, 319-323.

Taussig, Frederick J., *Abortion, Spontaneous and Induced*, C. V. Mosby, St. Louis, 1936.

Thom, Douglas A., *Everyday Problems of the Everyday Child*, Appleton, N. Y., 1927, p. 39.

General Reading List:

Bibby, Cyril, *How Life Is Handed On*, Emerson Books, N. Y., 1947.

Bibby, Cyril, *Sex Education: A Guide for Parents, Teachers, and Youth Leaders*, Emerson Books, N. Y., 1946.

Dennett, Mary Ware, *Sex Education of Children*, Vanguard, N. Y., 1931.

De Schweinitz, Karl, *Growing Up*, Macmillan, N. Y., 1928.

Gagliardo, Mrs. Ruth Garver, "We Wanted Children," *Parents Magazine*, Vol. XII, No. 5, May, 1937, p. 27.

Gruenberg, Benj. C., *Parents and Sex Education*, Viking Press, N. Y., 1932.

Moll, Albert, *The Sexual Life of the Child*, Macmillan, N. Y., 1929.

Richmond, Winifred, *An Introduction to Sex Education*, Farrar & Rinehart, N. Y., 1934.

Strain, Frances B., *New Patterns in Sex Education*, Appleton-Century, N. Y., 1935.

Strain, F. B., *Being Born*, Appleton-Century, N. Y., 1936.

Child Study.

Federal Children's Bureau Bulletins,
U. S. Department of Labor,
Washington, D. C.

Mental Hygiene.

Parents Magazine.

CHAPTER VIII

OVERCOMING SEXUAL MALADJUSTMENT

CHANGE AND GROWTH

Change and growth are inevitable facts in human
life, especially in marriage. It is not enough to
achieve sexual harmony early in marriage; a couple
must be ever on the alert to maintain it. What may
have been a satisfactory or tolerable situation in the
early months of marriage may be wholly unsatisfactory one year or ten years after. Some brides who
gladly share in the first few weeks of sexual experimentation lose interest after a time, if they are
unable to get a reasonable share of satisfaction out
of it. An unimaginative and self-satisfied bridegroom
may assume such lessened interest to be a change in
affection, but such is not necessarily the case. If there
is any unfavorable change in the zest for sexual
pleasures, it is well carefully to check over the situation and discover the possible cause.

MALADJUSTMENT IN WOMEN

During recent years specialists in the nervous diseases of women have come to recognize sexual maladjustment as one of the common causes of nervous
disorders. Not infrequently, a woman with an apparently sound constitution and no evidence of any
organic difficulty will report symptoms of indiges-

tion, sleeplessness, unexplainable fatigue, and irritability. One of the first procedures in such cases is to check on the sexual habits of the patient. Very often, all that is necessary to produce a cure is to make sure that she and her husband know how to obtain for her a fair degree of sexual satisfaction.

Through inexperience and lack of understanding many women fail to distinguish between the temporary thrill of sexual excitement and a complete orgasm which leaves them comfortably relaxed and soon ready for sleep.

"It is important also," says Dickinson, "that the couple have clearly in mind the difference between excitement or passionate desire and climax or orgasm. There is in women no such dramatic evidence of the latter as in men, with whom the emission and subsidence of erection give proof of completion. She may also require two or three minor orgasms to his one, to discharge the battery, and to this possibility his attention should be drawn."

When release is but partial, her sexual desire may be temporarily allayed, only to recur a short time later with increased intensity, or be converted into a nervous headache, a backache, or a dragging sense of bodily fatigue.

This failure to experience a satisfactory orgasm is not confined to "undersexed women." It may be found in women highly sensitive to sexual stimulation as well as in those of the so-called "frigid" type. Perhaps the former group are even more seriously affected by lack of orgasm than those less conscious of sexual feeling.

MALADJUSTMENT IN MEN

Unsatisfactory, infrequent, or too frequent sex experience may leave the husband irritated, dejected, and unreasonable, and unless he learns the true nature of his difficulty, and how to overcome it, the way is open for serious sexual incompatibility. The man who, for any of several reasons, may be unable to maintain an erection long enough to satisfy his wife is inclined to worry about it and develop an anxiety or an inferiority complex. This may not only affect his relations with his wife but seriously handicap him in all his activities. The man who finds his sexual desires are greatly in excess of his wife's wishes has his peace of mind disturbed in another way and the marriage and family relationship is put under special stress.

CAUSES OF MALADJUSTMENT

Among the more common causes of sexual disharmony in marriage are: (1) failure to appreciate the spiritual nature of marriage and to cooperate toward a common goal, (2) inadequate courting each time as a preliminary to sexual intercourse, (3) the practice of coitus interruptus (withdrawal), (4) premature ejaculation, (5) very unequal sex desire, (6) masturbation, (7) attempting intercourse when emotional and environmental conditions are not favorable, (8) the presence of certain psychic handicaps, (9) the natural consequences of specific physical changes in husband and wife, (10) conflicts in temperament.

Failure to Cooperate for a Common Goal

In general, it may be fairly said that failure to secure sexual satisfaction is evidence of the fact that a couple is not cooperating to the best advantage in this sphere of life. Whether this be due to ignorance or to some selfish purpose on the part of one or the other, the results are equally unhappy.

"Many a marriage," write the Elliotts, "is unsatisfactory because it fails to be a matter of mutual sharing. One mate adjusts completely to the other, or one learns to endure the other, but there is no mutual adjustment. . . . But, though a complete sharing of life's experiences is essential to any truly satisfying love relation, it is equally important that the couple come to their sexual relations on a high spiritual plane. . . .

"If sexual relations are carried on with no regard for the mate, with no love involved in the event, and with no art in the technique of intercourse, then they are not only unsatisfactory but they definitely lack spiritual quality. It is a physical union in a limited sense. But two people may, in giving themselves to each other in sexual intercourse, express their mutual love more completely than by any other method open to human beings. It is what two people bring to the event in the sharing of life and mutual love, and the artistry with which the love-making is carried on which determines its spiritual quality. . . .

"The first requisite is the recognition of the mutual character of the sex act. There is a false idea, fortunately less widely held than formerly, that women do not desire sexual relations, and that the wife merely tolerates them for the accommodation of her husband. The truth is that sexual desire is found in women as well as in men, and that the wife needs sexual relations as well as the husband. Further, if the wife does not enter fully into the relationship, sexual intercourse is not satisfactory to the husband, and it leaves the wife tense and frustrated, though she may not recognize the reason for her feelings. . . . As in all love relations, the skill in the courting and the degree to which the attention of each is focused upon the happiness of the other determines the quality of the relationship."

Inadequate Courting

In a large majority of cases the unsatisfactory sexual experiences reported by wives show a more or less uniform pattern of inadequate courting. "He just paws over me," and "He abruptly says, 'How about a party?'" are characteristic replies of two unhappy wives when asked to describe the meager preliminaries to sexual relations with their husbands. Such behavior fails to rise above the level of the higher animals, and is seldom adequate for a pleasing human response.

Every instance of sexual intimacy should be preceded by a courtship not unlike that before marriage, and involves the same sequence of events. The person initiating the courtship first, must attract the favorable attention of the other. This may be done by any of a thousand means, by words, looks, gifts, or acts which put him or her in a favorable light and make the giver seem a desirable person. Courtesy, kindness, generosity, appreciation, and even flattery are means by which one becomes a chosen person—one who has the liberty of touch and some measure of familiarity. Having won this position of advantage, the lover is ready to make use of endearing caresses. The gentle stroking of a hand, the brushing of a cheek, and the touch of warm lips, all serve to fuse mental and physical feeling into strong desire. It is not until both partners are eager for the full sexual embrace that the experience is likely to result in complete satisfaction.

Withdrawal

In most cases withdrawal (coitus interruptus) does not give the wife due consideration, since it is necessary to remove the penis before ejaculation occurs, when, as a rule, she is not yet ready for her climax and needs the assistance of the stiff male organ to complete it. Couples who find this procedure mutually satisfactory are entitled to their preference but it cannot be recommended for the average pair.

Premature Ejaculation

This is a common difficulty with many couples in the early weeks of sexual activity, and often carries over for months or years because they do not know how to correct it before it becomes a habit pattern. Its correction usually lies in giving special attention to one or more of the following difficulties: (1) too much mental stimulation in the husband due to prolonged anticipation, or too much caressing and contact stimulation before attempting to make the actual penetration, (2) friction on the glans penis at penetration, due to insufficient lubrication of the vaginal opening, (3) failure to rest for a brief period after making the entrance, or (4) some structural condition requiring the attention and advice of a physician or specialist in sexual ailments. Usually these difficulties can be overcome by patient and intelligent care, and the reward will be found well worth the effort.

(1) Some men find that it is impossible for them to do very much handling and caressing of their wives without becoming so sexually stimulated that orgasm becomes involuntary, sometimes even without actual union. Not infrequently this is a passing phase of psychological adjustment to the novelty of early marital intimacies. Occasionally it may be charged to a state of mind growing out of old inhibitions, or to habits of speedy release in the practice of masturbation. A change in the form of caressing, or some limitation of the time and circumstance often helps to correct this condition. Where the difficulty persists, the man should consult a physician and make sure there is no organic difficulty. If there is no organic difficulty then the treatment will be confined to psychological guidance.

(2) Insufficient lubrication of the vaginal entrance results in friction between the surface of the vulva and the penis. This is not only uncomfortable for the woman, but may set up intense localized stimulation of the nerves in the glans, and so bring on premature orgasm in the man. Even with adequate lubrication this may take place in the early

days of marriage before the vaginal opening has become sufficiently stretched to make the entrance easy. A gentle investigation with the forefinger in the vaginal folds before attempting to make the entrance will usually be sufficient to test for ample lubrication. If the woman's glands do not seem able to supply the natural moisture, an artificial lubricant may be applied, preferably a *greaseless water-soluble* lubricating jelly. It is put up in several convenient-sized collapsible metal tubes and may be purchased under various trade names at most drug stores. It is much more satisfactory than the petroleum jellies or other oily substances, because it is not so messy and does not create laundering problems, however freely it is used.

(3) To rest a few moments after completing the entrance often serves to check the rising tide of sexual excitement just enough to give the man greater voluntary control of ejaculation. Progress and improvement may be slow at first, but if the husband will give careful attention to each detail of the process and avoid haste and friction, he will find, in most cases, a gradual lengthening of the period between entrance and orgasm. This makes possible continued increase of the woman's stimulation until she is more nearly ready for orgasm.

(4) In cases where either partner has peculiar structural conditions, it is important to consult a physician if any difficulty is encountered which continues to cause trouble. It is worth the price of a specialist's fee to secure an early diagnosis and treat-

ment for difficulties in this phase of life. If the problem has not been recognized and corrected before marriage, certainly it should not be allowed to create a barrier against mutual adjustment by further neglect.

The wife who fails to secure her orgasm as a consequence of the practice of withdrawal or premature ejaculation has several choices open to her. She may prefer to do nothing on occasions when not already highly stimulated, but if she is well along toward an orgasm, this course may leave her tense and nervous. At such times one of the following procedures may prove helpful.

(1) After the husband withdraws, the wife's stimulation may be continued until orgasm by stroking the clitoris and vulva with a finger, varying the pressure and speed in such a manner as to keep the tide of feeling rising to a climax. Considerable practice and patience may be necessary to learn how to accomplish this in a satisfactory manner, but many couples have found it a necessary substitute for mutual orgasm.

(2) In the case of premature ejaculation this same procedure may be followed while the penis is still in the vagina and before the woman's stimulation has subsided. If preferred, the penis may be withdrawn at once and the stimulation of the clitoris continued as above.

The morality of using such auxiliary methods of continuing the woman's stimulation to secure her orgasm has long been recognized by church and medical authorities. The Roman Catholic Church specifically sanctions such procedure in the marriage relation when used to supplement normal sex relationships between husband and wife. Inasmuch as Nature has not endowed woman with the automatic release which man has, it stands to reason that when her nerves, her mental poise, and even her love-life are at stake, some such means of relief is necessary and commendable.

(3) The couple may shift to the wife-above position so that the woman is able to secure the correct pressure of the clitoris against the man's pubic eminence, leg, or body and continue the necessary friction to produce her orgasm.

(4) Should the woman's stimulation slump and her desire fade away during any part of the process before she has reached her orgasm it is best to stop and relax as completely as possible. After a period of rest, sometimes several hours later, her sexual desire is likely to return in full force. Under such circumstances she is likely to reach her orgasm more easily than usual and her husband more apt to have better control of the ejaculation than previously.

Unequal Desire

Studies of American marriage behavior show a wide variation in the frequency of intercourse. As has already been pointed out, some couples average less than once a month while others seem to thrive on once a day or oftener. Davis was unable to discover that the less frequent group was any less

happy than the other. Whether such variation is
due to glandular or temperamental differences, it
can be readily seen that if a "sexual athlete" marries a frigid or impotent individual some drastic
adjustment will be necessary before their personal
"needs" or desires can be accommodated. Without
the sympathetic understanding that such differences are natural and that there are ways by which
most such disparities can be adjusted, some measure
of sexual incompatibility is almost certain to develop.

In some cases something can be done through
proper medication and the use of supplementary
glandular extracts. Aside from medical treatment
there are two types of adjustment which may
afford real relief for such unequally matched couples. One is a change in *mental expectation;* the
other is a change in *sexual behavior.* Neither
partner should be expected to make all the adjustments but each should strive to approach the desires
of the other so that the final arrangement does not
make excessive demands on either. The following two
cases illustrate such adjustments.

Mrs. H., whose religious belief limited permissible
sex relations when she did not wish a child to a three-
day "safe-time" period toward the end of her
monthly cycle, married a man who desired such relations several times a week. There was a battle for
years until the woman was advised by her counselor
that it was safe for her to increase the number of
"free days" and proper to use finger stimulation as a
supplementary means of producing the orgasm when

necessary. She was thus enabled to accommodate her husband with increased satisfaction to herself without disregarding the teaching of her church in matters of birth control or sex behavior.

Mr. S. was a man of considerable creative genius married to a charming and vivacious woman with a pronounced crest of sexual desire both before and after her menstrual period. He insisted on a separate room, separate bath, and objected to being disturbed day or night while engaged in his work. After the first year or two intimacies came only at intervals of three or four months and these only under some unusual circumstance during which his creative interests were thrown aside and he was open to the normal responses of intimate married living.

Meanwhile his wife was so tormented by recurrent desire that she felt compelled to seek out other men or make use of self-release, neither of which was pleasing to her. A more satisfactory adjustment was arranged wherein the husband should recognize the wife's need, and more holiday trips might be planned during which romance might run its natural course.

Women of inadequate desire ordinarily can learn to increase their frequency without difficulty, provided the couple knows how to make each occasion a mutually satisfying experience. The recollection and anticipation of such experiences are usually much more helpful to the undersexed, as a means of stimulation, than any particular change in mechanical technique. The spirit of glad wishing for such increased enjoyment is of untold value to the wife who is seeking to keep her husband happy and contented.

Women whose glandular capacity and desire is greater than that of their husbands have a more difficult problem. If they are not busy with the care of children, or with other serious and interesting work, it is easy for them to become preoccupied with sexual emotions and thus increase rather than decrease their difficulty. While interesting and creative activity may help, something more than being busy is necessary to adjust such marriages to a smoothly running tempo. When the husband feels unequal to bring his wife relief in the usual manner he will find that with a little practice he can help her secure the orgasm by extra-vaginal procedures, all the while conserving the spiritual values of mutual caressing and demonstrations of affection. If the husband is not available some form of self-relief is to be preferred to spending sleepless nights and irritable days under the tension of unrelieved glandular stimulation.

Men who seem undersexed may be so because they have inherited a low glandular capacity, or they may be mentally worried, physically run-down, or intellectually overworked. Glandular extracts properly administered by a skilled physician may sometimes help the man with a low sexual output. Careful attention to the rules of mental hygiene can restore in a large measure the sexual vigor of an enervated husband. Pearl holds that mechanics, farmers, and laborers, all of whom are engaged in vigorous muscular activity, have less trouble with sexual impotence than do men engaged in the more sedentary and intellectual pursuits. Often a real vacation, with a well balanced program of rest and activity, will help to restore the impaired vigor of a deficient husband.

Highly sexed men, such as those reported in the Davis study, with records of daily intercourse for periods of twenty years or more, are not always fortunate in finding wives who can match them in sexual ability. While it may be easier for a woman to increase her frequency than for a man his, there are limits beyond which human nerves and emotions cannot be pushed without danger and dissatisfaction.

For those times when husband or wife is not available a resort to self-relief by manual friction may be advisable if the sexual tension is such as to interfere with sleep or necessary mental concentration. Care needs to be taken lest such relief become a habit which is self-centered only, and conflicts with the best control of orgasm during the process of normal intercourse. It will help also to avoid as far as possible all artificial stimulation, such as the reading of erotic literature, indulging in daydreams and sex talk, and looking at suggestive pictures or theatricals. When necessary, self-release is physically as legitimate as the use of sedatives, but like them, should not be permitted to become a fixed habit.

Masturbation

There are three types of masturbation which may seriously interfere with attaining normal sex satisfaction in marriage. In the absence of any very accurate data on the actual results from the practice of masturbation one may not be too positive as to effects in a given case, but the following statements are not far from the facts.

(1) The tendency of many boys who practice masturbation is to produce the orgasm as quickly as possible, there being little incentive for prolonging its coming. This tendency to speed up the orgasm leads, we think, towards premature ejaculation rather than towards that longer self-control which is usually needed to produce the woman's orgasm. If masturbation has been continued in this fashion for several years immediately preceding marriage it may well be expected that it will require time to change the male responses better to accommodate the woman's needs.

(2) Some girls practice a type of masturbation which affords considerable excitation of the vulva and clitoris but falls short of orgasm. Others secure the orgasm by stimulation of the clitoris. In either case, when a girl who has long practiced this form of stimulation marries, she is likely to find either that she is unable to get beyond a certain point of external stimulation and quite unable to allow the full development of the orgasm, or that she can secure the orgasm only by finger stimulation. The practice of "clamping down" on one's sexual expression at a certain point of stimulation becomes a serious handicap when carried over into the marriage experience.

(3) In a similar way the girl who engages in

"heavy petting" to the point of mutual masturbation which habitually *stops short of orgasm* often finds, on entering marriage, that she has built up an unconscious barrier to full sexual release. The girl who has allowed her lover to excite her just so far, and then stops short for fear of the consequences, builds a pattern of response which, if long continued, will be difficult to change in married life. She will get just so far with her excitation and then find it impossible to get beyond that to full orgasm. It requires clear understanding of the problem and the patient cooperation of both husband and wife to build new patterns of response and make possible a full and satisfying sex life.

Unfavorable Conditions

Under average conditions almost any man or any woman can be interested in sexual play at any time by the loving and tactful approach of the beloved if the place and circumstances be appropriate. There are times and circumstances, however, which are distinctly less favorable than others for such activities, and attempts to initiate sexual courtship on these less favorable occasions are likely to result in failure. Indispositions such as colds, fatigue, worry, anger, jealousy, and various forms of disappointment, tend commonly to be a handicap to full and spontaneous response.

If one is "all stuffed up" with a sniffly cold he is seldom in a mood for sexual indulgence. The same is true of marked fatigue or any other emotional state. One needs to be somewhat near the normal, undisturbed state of being to engage in these activities with ease and emotional profit.

Occasionally there may be an exception to this general principle. Just as a child, in times of grief or trouble, may turn to his mother for consolation and enjoy being cuddled and petted, and will return the expressions of love and sympathy, so husband and wife, when tired and troubled, may find peace and relaxation in being cuddled and caressed. Under some circumstances this may lead to mutual desire for complete sexual union. When such a situation develops it should be recognized as a very natural one, and carried forward to its natural conclusion. Except in cases of illness, the consoling partner may even be justified in subtly tempting the other into sexual activity as an effective means of diversion and relaxation.

Psychic Handicaps

Failure to make satisfactory adjustment in the conjugal relations of marriage is often due to a wrong mental attitude carried over from earlier days rather than to wrong technical procedure.

"It may be that the woman is, for the time being, prevented from having an orgasm because as a child or an adolescent she was trained to think of sex as evil, or was attacked by a boy, or was otherwise shocked, and thus inwardly frozen or inhibited. The ordinary methods of arousing the wife in such cases may not avail. It is first of all necessary for the husband to release his wife from the fears and feelings of taboo that prevent her from experiencing the orgasm. One of the best ways to release her is for the husband himself, during the early days of the honeymoon, to share with his wife all the experiences, anxieties about sex play, and struggles he passed through as a boy, adolescent, and young man. This, incidentally, will help to free him from the inhibitions which most people carry into marriage. But most of all it will encourage his wife to look back upon her childhood experiences and see how she has perhaps become frigid and frustrated because of some deeply imbedded and probably forgotten emotional conditioning. He must also get her to see that she is not unique and alone; on the contrary, many have had to go through the same difficulties. If she can so thoroughly trust her husband and feel so utterly at home with him, that she can not only trace back these experiences but also live them through again emotionally, then there is a fair chance that by so doing, she can become liberated, and thus have done for her what the psychoanalyst would perhaps charge thousands of dollars to accomplish. This sharing of experiences may not only release both husband and wife, but enhance and strengthen the whole marriage relationship." Dr. Alan Hunter, Hollywood, Calif.

In addition to the fears and inhibitions growing out of past experiences, there are often anxieties which arise out of false expectations. The gossip of relatives and friends often gives to brides and grooms erroneous impressions as to what marriage may be like. Girls whose mothers have looked upon sexual relations in marriage with embittered toleration, or deep resentment, often carry over into their own marriages something of the same point of view. Persons who bring to marriage certain fixed and arbitrary standards as to the proper times, places, frequency, and procedures for sexual intercourse are likely to have difficulty when face to face with actual marriage situations. It might easily be expected that the bride who had never dreamed of having sexual intercourse at any other time or place than at night and in bed, would be shocked and unable to respond freely when tempted to indulge under other circumstances. As has been suggested in Chapter II, any sense of guilt, or shame, or any sort of fear may so inhibit one or both partners that the total experience will be unsatisfactory.

Physical Changes

Among the factors which affect the sexual relations of husbands and wives adversely are certain physical changes incidental to more or less normal human life and due neither to ignorance nor bad mental hygiene. Among these are such things as pregnancy, surgical operations, illness, and the menopause or change of life in the woman. In later life certain ailments of the prostate in men may incapacitate them for sexual intercourse. To understand the nature and consequence of these conditions is to open the way for a practical adjustment to them.

Pregnancy introduces both physical and mental changes which may seriously affect the love life of a couple unless they understand the situation and plan their relations accordingly. While some women during the period are averse to having sexual relations, others find their desire especially strong at times and are most happy to express their affection and joy over the coming of the child by sharing with its father this most intimate and pleasurable of all physical contacts. The woman's condition and desire should always determine the procedure. As has already been explained, sexual relations may be continued for the greater part of the period, care being taken to avoid those particular weeks during which she would have been menstruating had she not become pregnant. For the first few months in particular these special days are those during which a miscarriage is most likely to occur. If the usual husband-above position is uncomfortable one of the modified forms of intercourse may be substituted. In case of any uncertainty the advice of the physician should be specifically asked.

Operations. Occasionally some disease of the uterus, vagina, or vulva requires extensive surgical treatment. In some cases the entire uterus is removed and the vagina left in as near its natural shape as possible. After such operations, however, intercourse is likely to be painful and less satisfactory than usual until the severed nerve endings have had a chance to lose some of their sensitivity and the raw edges of the scars have fully healed. Often this full process takes several months. Even after the parts seem wholly adjusted to normal conditions the tensions of sexual stimulation may cause severe pain.

Under such circumstances the husband ought to forego all attempts to initiate sexual relations for several months, leaving his wife free to invite his sexual approach whenever she wishes to experiment and determine the degree of her recovery.

Childbirth. Occasionally after childbirth it is many weeks before the woman is able to respond freely to her husband's sexual caresses. However difficult it may be for him, it is important that he remain as patient and as considerate as he was during their honeymoon. Should their attempts at intercourse prove to be painful to her in spite of his most careful attentions, a physician should be consulted. There may be some structural or other condition present which can be easily corrected. Special care needs to be taken to avoid times of fatigue in such cases, experimenting only when the wife is rested and quite willing.

Illness. Few people become suddenly ill. There is usually a period when they are "coming down" with the disease. During such a time they are in no better mood for work or for vigorous activity than when they are convalescing from an illness. Fever, headache, irritability, and weariness are common signs of an impending illness and one should not expect a partner to be sexually responsive when he or she feels out of sorts. After any illness it is a good rule to let the person who has been ill take the initiative toward the renewal of sexual relations.

The Menopause. A New York judge tells of a case in the domestic relations court where a man and his wife had been having trouble, and in court the man complained that his wife had recently been "cold and distant" toward him. After a little inquiry the judge sent them both to a physician and in about

fifteen minutes the verdict came back, "Menopause."
Here was a husband who was unaware of the fact
that,

"Sometime between the ages of forty and fifty-five
every woman goes through a tremendously important
period of physiological and psychological change called the
menopause, the climacteric, or 'the change of life.' . . .
"The change of life is a period varying in duration from
a few months to a year or more, during which the female
reproductive organs undergo certain profound changes.
The uterus, or womb, and the ovaries become smaller.
The thyroid gland undergoes certain modifications which
make it less active. As a result, the entire glandular balance of the body is upset, and with this upset concomitant
changes take place in the mental and physical and
emotional constitution. Usually there is a slowing down
of the tempo of life, a disposition of fat, notably on the
buttocks, a gradual diminution of the menstruation with,
finally, its complete cessation. . . . In the mental sphere
there is a well-marked tendency to irascibility, worry,
over-sensitivity, introspection, depression, and sometimes
fairly marked changes in the ability to pay attention,
remember, and concentrate on immediate problems. The
emotional changes may run the entire gamut from extreme
sexual passion to complete sexual apathy, from querulous-
ness and self-pity to stoical impassivity.' . . .
"There is no earthly reason why any woman today, who
can get to a reputable gynecologist, internist, or well-
conducted woman's clinic, should ever suffer from the
terrors that beset her mother and grandmother during the
menopause.' . . .
"There is widespread belief that the menopause means
not only the cessation of childbearing but the cessation of
sexual attractiveness and sexual interest. Nothing can be
further from the truth. The woman who desires and needs
active sexual life will find sexual relations just as satisfying after the menopause as before it. . . . Sexual attractiveness is not a matter of youth and physique: it is

certainly just as much a matter of psychological readiness
and cooperation. The woman who has lived a normal
sexual life, who has been married and borne children, will
find no terrors in her menopause if she will only realize
that the investments in comradeship and cooperation
which she made during her active sexual life will begin to
bear dividends at this time."

Some men, between forty and sixty, go through
a glandular change scarcely less striking than that of
the woman. Sometimes the prostate gland is seriously
affected and sexual vigor considerably diminished.
Any soreness or other marked change in potency
should be reported to an experienced physician,
preferably a trained urologist. With good general
health most men retain a fair measure of sexual vigor
well up through the sixties and seventies.

If either husband or wife undergoes any marked
physical or glandular change a physician should be
consulted so as to take any advantage there may be
in adequate medical care. A complete physical examination somewhere around the age of forty is a
wise precaution for both men and women to forestall
any unfavorable tendencies in bodily health.

Conflicts in Temperament

The causes of marital maladjustment are not always
to be found either in physical and material handicaps,
or even in the lack of sexual satisfaction. It is probably true that temperamental differences lead to sexual dissatisfaction as often as sexual dissatisfaction
reveals itself in temperamental outbursts. Certainly
we know that these two factors in human life are

closely interwoven, even though we may not always say with assurance which is cause and which is effect.

Undoubtedly each person is born with certain temperamental qualities which are developed and modified to some degree as he grows to maturity. If a couple has not given this matter of temperamental congeniality rather careful consideration during the days of courtship and early marriage it is quite possible that habits and dispositions which were negligible and inoffensive at first, may later become very annoying.

"Stop it!" shrieked the angry wife to her silent husband.

"Why, my dear, I haven't said anything for an hour or more," he replied.

"No, but you've been listening in a most annoying manner."

One's attitude may speak volumes.

Whenever a couple tends to get on one another's nerves, or when one tends to be continuously critical of the other, then it is time for them to take stock of their relationship and see what can be done to restore it to a state of harmony. If, after earnest, but unsuccessful attempts at adjustment, a couple would take their difficulties to a well trained and experienced counselor much sorrow and many broken homes could be saved.

COUNSELORS

In times of personal perplexity it is worth almost anything to be able to talk things over with some

trustworthy and understanding person. Whom
should one seek on such an occasion?

Before taking one's troubles outside the family it
is best for husband and wife to face these squarely
themselves. To dodge or to evade difficulties or to
shout them from the house-tops to neighbors or relatives is perhaps the worst way to approach a happy
solution. A frank facing and settling of problems
as they arise is usually the best way to get along
happily.

Relatives

Sometimes a kindly and sensible relative can be fair
and unemotional in his judgment and so able to
help work out a satisfactory solution. But when a
problem is so charged with emotion and complexity
that a husband and wife cannot deal with it successfully by themselves, it is seldom a question to be
handled by relatives on either side.

Pastors

Within recent years more and more pastors of
various faiths have become expert in dealing with
all sorts of human perplexities, including sexual
difficulties. Many of these pastors are accustomed to
hearing confessions of blundering and are not as
critical and fault-finding as is sometimes supposed.
Most of them have excellent contacts with good physicians, psychologists, and other expert advisors and,
if the problem is one they cannot handle themselves,
they will be glad to refer cases to such professional
advisors.

Physicians

During recent years medical schools and research clinics have tended to extend medical service somewhat beyond the mere treatment of organic disease. A few men and more women are finding it profitable to become skilled in such matters as contraception, pre-marital examinations, sexual hygiene, and psychological adjustment. Not every physician is skilled in this field but in many communities the physician is the most likely person to whom one might go for the adjustment of sexual problems.

Psychologists and Psychoanalysts

Some psychologists and psychoanalysts have done excellent work; others attempting to do work in these fields are not only poorly trained but exceedingly narrow and one-sided in their approach to social problems. Psychoanalysts usually require from one hundred to four hundred visits of an hour or more, and as a result such treatment is expensive. In selecting one it is best, first, to discover his or her personal standing in the community and in the profession. Most universities, child guidance clinics, mental hygiene centers, maternal health bureaus, and marriage guidance institutes can put one in touch with competent practitioners in these fields.

Psychiatrists

A psychiatrist is a physician who has had a certain special training for dealing with cases of mental disorder which are largely outside the educational field. When persons are so disturbed emotionally or mentally that they cannot follow a guidance program of their own volition, then their case is one for a psychiatrist. While the psychiatrist charges a specialist's fee, in many cases his help is more effective and less expensive in the long run than that of some less expert practitioner.

Marriage Counselors

In many cities there have been set up in the past few years marriage guidance centers for advising those who have personal and family difficulties. As a rule the person in charge of these centers is a fairly competent advisor on marriage problems. The best way to protect oneself from the occasional "quack" is to inquire of some pastor, teacher, or reputable and informed business or professional person and discover the standing of such a counselor or institution before taking one's troubles to them.

Lawyers

Some attorneys are well versed, not only in the legal aspects of family relationships, but also appreciate some of the social relationships which are of vital importance to successful married living. If one has a confidential relationship with a trusted attorney it may be a good plan to present to him an intimate problem. Often he will be able either to advise one directly or to suggest some more expert counselor to whom one can go with confidence.

In conclusion it may well be said that often good medicine is not easy to take. Mistakes and blunders are not always easy to correct. Those who experience trouble must be prepared to face out their difficulties courageously and be willing to follow patiently a line of guidance suggested by the counselor to whom they go in times of perplexity.

MARRIED WISDOM

1. Don't ever both get angry at the same time.
2. Never talk at one another, either alone or in company.
3. Never speak loudly to one another, unless the house is on fire.
4. Never find fault unless it is perfectly certain that a fault has been committed, and always speak lovingly.
5. Never taunt with a mistake.
6. Never make a remark at the expense of each other —it is a meanness.
7. Never part for a day without loving words to think of during absence.
8. Never let the sun go down upon any anger or grievance.
9. Never meet without a loving welcome.
10. Never let any fault you have committed go by, until you have frankly confessed it and asked forgiveness.
11. Never forget the happy hours of early love.
12. Never sigh over what might have been, but make the best of what is.

Author unknown.

REFERENCES

Broadhead, Geo. L., M.D., *Approaching Motherhood*, Hoeber, N. Y., 1930.

Craissons, Vicar General D., *De Rebus Venereis ad usum Confessariorum*, Paris, France, 1870, p. 172.

Davis, Katherine B., *Sex Factors in the Lives of 2200 Women*, Harpers, N. Y., 1929, p 21.

Dickinson, R. L., "Premarital Examination," *American Journal Obstetrics and Gynecology*, November, 1928.

Dickinson, R. L., and Beam, Lura, *One Thousand Marriages, Passim*, Williams and Wilkins, Baltimore, 1931, *Passim*.

Dickinson, R. L., and Bryant, Louise, *The Control of Conception*, Williams and Wilkins, Baltimore, 1931, p. 57.

Elliott, Harrison S. and Grace L., *Solving Personal Problems*, Holt, N. Y., 1936, pp. 161, 163, 164, 165.

Heaton, Claude E., M.D., *Modern Motherhood*, Farrar & Rinehart, N. Y., 1935.

Irving, Frederick C., *The Expectant Mother's Handbook*, Riverside Press, N. Y., 1932.

Pearl, Raymond, *The Biology of Population Growth*, Knopf, N. Y., 1925, pp. 202-204.

Slater, Fr. Thomas, S.J., *Manual of Moral Theology*, 2 Vols., Benziger Bros., N. Y., 1908, Vol. 2, pp. 361-365.

Stone, Chester T., *The Dangerous Age in Men*, Macmillan, N. Y., 1935.

Wolfe, Beran, *A Woman's Best Years*, Emerson Books, N. Y., 1933, pp. 37-44.

The illustrations that follow are the work of Dr. Robert L. Dickinson. These diagrams, together with the explanations that accompany them, are here reproduced by his permission.

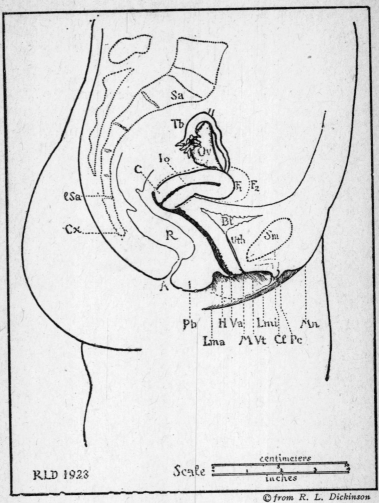

RLD 1923

Scale

centimeters

inches

© from R. L. Dickinson

P L A T E I

168

PLATE I—EXPLANATION   169

FEMALE ORGANS, SIDE VIEW
Slightly more than one third life size

A vertical section through the middle of the body. The generative organs are shown in heavy outline; the urinary organs and other parts of the body in lighter outline.

BONES

The bones are indicated by dotted lines.

Sa—lsa, Sacrum, the largest of the bones at the base of the spine.

Cx, Coccyx, the tip-end bone of the spine.

Sm, Symphysis, the front meeting place of the bony girdle, or pelvis.

EXCRETORY ORGANS

R, Rectum, which carries away the solid waste matter from the bowels.

A, Anus, the opening of the rectum.

Bl, Bladder, which holds the waste water, or urine. Here shown empty; when full of fluid, it is much larger and balloon shaped.

Uth, Urethra, the tube which carries away the urine.

M, Meatus, or opening of the urethra.

SEX ORGANS (INTERNAL)

Ov, Ovary in which the egg or ovum grows. There are two ovaries, one at either side and above the uterus.

Tb, Fallopian Tube, which carries the ovum to the uterus. There are two tubes, one leading from each ovary.

U, Uterus, or Womb, in which the egg or ovum becomes an embryo and grows into a baby.

F_1, Fundus, or top of the womb.

F_2 indicates the increase in size of the uterus, after a woman has had a baby.

C, Cervix, the neck of the uterus, through which the semen has to go, on its way to meet the ovum.

Va, Vagina, or Birth Canal, which leads out from the uterus, and into which the penis fits during the sex act. Here shown at rest or closed, the front and back walls lying almost together, so it looks like a slim tube with irregularly wrinkled sides. During sex union, it is distended and becomes round, with a diameter of an inch and a quarter or more.

SEX ORGANS (EXTERNAL)

This group of parts is called the Vulva.

H, Hymen, the membrane which, in the virginal state, partly closes the entrance to the vagina.

Cl, Clitoris, the miniature equivalent of the male organ, the penis. It is mostly hidden under the

PLATE I—EXPLANATION (CONTINUED) 171

skin, as indicated by the faint dotted line, but it enlarges when stimulated by the sex act.

Pc, Prepuce or Foreskin of the clitoris. (See Plate II).

Lma, Labia Majora, the rounded outer lips of the vulva, or portal of the sex organs.

Lmi, Labia Minora, the thin inner lips of the vulva. (See Plate II).

Mn, Mons Veneris, or cushion over the bone *Sm,* symphysis. This cushion is covered with hair which is not shown in the diagram.

Pb, Perineum. The muscles and tendons which center here hold up all the lower organs, but they relax during the birth of the baby.

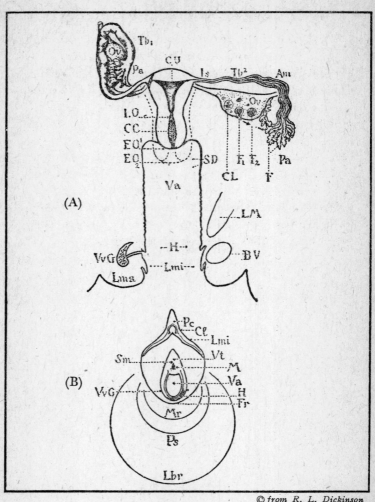

(A)

(B)

© from R. L. Dickinson

PLATE II

172

PLATE II—EXPLANATION   173

(A) FEMALE ORGANS, FRONT VIEW
(B) DIAGRAM OF THE VULVA

Slightly more than one third life size

(A). The ovary and tube on the left side of the drawing are shown in the true position; on the right side they are spread out and cut in two, to show the inside.

(B). The upper part shows the outline of the external genital parts, drawn open. The lower curves indicate the extent to which the vaginal opening can enlarge to permit sex union and birth.

———————

(A) Ov, Ovary. The one at the left side of the drawing is in natural position and shows the outside. The one on the right side is laid sideways and cut in two, to show the inside.

Tb_1, Fallopian Tube, outside view. Tb_2, Fallopian Tube, inside view.

F_1, Follicle or Sac, from which the ovum or egg has just escaped. The tiny dots behind each arrow indicate its course into the tube. The egg is like the dot on a small letter i, just visible.

F_2, Follicle, closed, the dot inside indicating the egg which will be freed from its sac a month later.

Cl, Corpus Luteum, or yellow body, the empty puckered sac remaining from the previous month.

Pa, Pavillion, the trumpet-shaped, leaf-like end of the tube, where the egg enters after leaving the ovary. F, the fringe-like tips of the tube.

Am, Ampulla, the widened fluted part of the tube.

Is, Isthmus, the narrowest part of the tube, the inner passage of which is no larger than a bristle, just wide enough for the minute egg to pass. The meeting place of the egg and the sperm cells is between Is and Pa. The egg is pushed along the tube for three days till it reaches the uterus.

U_1, Uterus, showing its virginal proportions.

U_2, shows by dotted line the size of the womb, after having borne a child. It never shrinks fully back to its virginal size.

CU, Cavity of the Uterus, with front half cut away to show the inside.

PLATE II—EXPLANATION (CONTINUED) 175

IO, Internal Os, or inner mouth, which divides the uterus into two parts. It is in the cavity above this inner mouth that the egg becomes an embryo and grows into a baby.

CC, Cavity of the Cervix, or neck of the uterus.

EO_1, External Os, or mouth of the womb.

EO_2, indicating size after child-bearing.

SD, Upper part of the Vagina, where the semen is deposited by the male.

Va, Vagina, distended as in sex union.

LM, Levator Muscle, which circles and closes the vagina. There are two of them, only one being shown.

H, Hymen, open as in intercourse.

VvG, Vulvo-Vaginal Gland, which furnishes lubrication during the sex act.

BV, Bulb of the Vestibule, a bunch of veins that, like the clitoris, enlarges from excitement.

Lmi, Labia Minora, the inner lips of the entrance to the vagina.

Lma, Labia Majora, the outer lips.

(B) *Cl*, Clitoris, the small penis-like organ, which enlarges under excitement.

Pc, Prepuce, or Foreskin of the clitoris.

Lmi, Labia Minora, here shown drawn apart.

Fr, Fourchette, or fork, a fold that appears when the vulva is spread open.

Va, Vagina, which leads to the uterus.

H, Hymen, here shown expanded and drawn apart. In repose it puckers in and closes, so that the vaginal opening hardly shows.

Vt, Vestibule, an oval space in the upper part of which is the

M, Meatus, the opening of the urethra or water-passage.

VvG, Vulvo-vaginal, or lubricating glands.

Mr, indicates the size of the vaginal opening during intercourse.

Ps, shows the size it may reach in a woman who has had children.

Lbr, indicates the expansion when birth occurs. This largest circle permits the passage of the baby's head, which is the largest and hardest part of a new-born baby; the bones of the baby's skull are loosely joined, so that they can be overlapped somewhat during the birth. There is always what is called the "soft spot" on top of a baby's head, but as the child grows the joints of the skull become firm and hard.

PLATE II—EXPLANATION (CONTINUED)   177

Sm, indicates the position of the symphysis, or front joining of the bony arch of the pelvis, under which the baby's head slips out during the birth process.

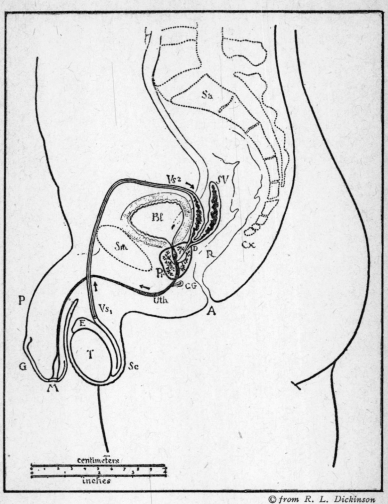

centimeters

inches

PLATE III

178

© from R. L. Dickinson

PLATE III—EXPLANATION   179

MALE ORGANS, SIDE VIEW

Slightly more than one third life size

A vertical section through the middle of the body. The generative organs are shown in heavy outline; the urinary organs and other parts of the body in lighter outline.

BONES

The bones are indicated by dotted lines.

Sa, Sacrum, the largest of the bones at the end of the spine.

Cx, Coccyx, the tip-end bone of the spine.

Sm, Symphysis, the front meeting place of the bony girdle or pelvis.

EXCRETORY ORGANS

R, Rectum, which carries away the solid waste matter from the bowels.

A, Anus, the opening of the rectum.

Bl, Bladder, which holds the waste water or urine. Here shown nearly empty. When full it is much larger.

SEX ORGANS

P, Penis, which fits into the vagina during the sex act. It is here shown relaxed.

G, Glans and Prepuce, or Foreskin.

Uth, Urethra, the passage which carries away the waste water or urine, and through which also the germs of life pass during the sex act. The urethra is here shown empty. Plate IV shows it distended.

T, Testicle, of which there are two, and in which grow the spermatozoa, or germs of life. The arrows in the drawing show the course of the spermatozoa. (For an interior view, see Plate IV.)

Sc, Scrotum, the bag which holds the testicles.

E, Epididymis, where the spermatozoa are finished. (See Plate IV.)

Vs_1 and Vs_2, Vas Deferens, which carry the spermatozoa to the urethra. There are two of these tubes, one from each testicle.

SV, Seminal Vesicle, of which there are two, one on either side of the bladder.

Pr, Prostate Gland, cut across to show the inside. The seminal vesicles and the prostate gland each secrete liquids forming the bulk of the semen and which act as carriers and stimulants for the spermatozoa.

D, Ejaculatory Duct, which expels the spermatozoa at the climax of the sex act.

PLATE III—EXPLANATION (CONTINUED) 181

CG, Cowper's Gland, a tiny gland furnishing lubricant and alkaline secretion the function of which
is obscure.

(Plate IV shows the spermatozoa, greatly magnified.)

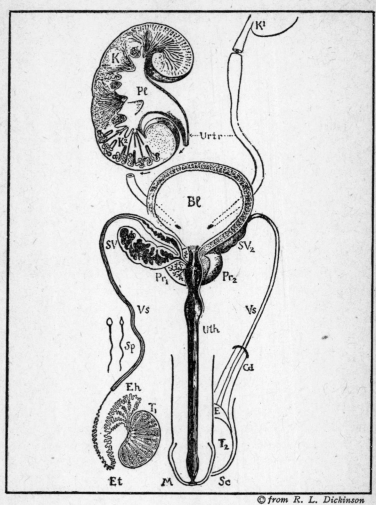

PLATE IV
182

PLATE IV—EXPLANATION 183

MALE ORGANS, FRONT VIEW
Slightly more than one third life size.

The male sex organs and the urinary organs are closely related, so this plate includes the kidney, which collects the urine or waste water and the two ureters which convey it to the bladder, where it is held till it is passed from the body.

On the right side of the diagram, the lower part of the kidney is outlined, but to save space is placed nearer to the bladder than it actually is, the ureter being really ten inches long. On the left side the other kidney is shown in its right size in relation to the other organs, but not in its proper place which is ten inches higher. It is cut in two, to show the inside.

EXCRETORY ORGANS

K_1, outline of the lower part of the Kidney.

K, the Kidney cut open to show the structure.

K_2, the minute Kidney structure, greatly enlarged.

Pl, the basin where the urine collects.

$Urtr$, Ureters, which carry the urine to the bladder. They are actually about 10 inches long, but are here shortened to save space.

Bl, Bladder, not distended. The dotted lines lead to the openings of the two ureters.

SEX ORGANS

Uth, Urethra, shown distended.

M, Meatus, the opening of the urethra, through which both the urine and the semen are passed.

T_1, Testicle, turned sideways and cut across to show where, in minute ducts in compartments, the spermatozoa are manufactured.

T_2, Testicle, hanging in place in the scrotum.

Sc, Scrotum.

E, Epididymis. Outside. (See Plate III.)

Eh, Epididymis head. ⎫ Inside view, spread out to
Et, Epididymis tail. ⎬ show structure.

Vs, Vas Deferens, or Seminal Duct, leading to ejaculatory duct (see Plate III). On the left side it is shown cut across to reveal the tiny tube which carries the spermatozoa.

Cd, Spermatic Cord, made up of muscles, nerves and blood vessels, in which the vas deferens runs through the opening in the abdominal wall into the interior of the abdomen. The actual length of the vas deferens is about eighteen inches. The diagram foreshortens it to save space. A third is convoluted. The wide terminal portion (ampulla) is now known to be the reservoir for spermatozoa.

SV, Seminal Vesicle, cut across to show the inside, and pulled to one side, to show the form.

PLATE IV—EXPLANATION (CONTINUED) 185

SV_2, Seminal Vesicle, outside view, and shown in its proper place behind the bladder.

Pr_1, Prostate Gland, cut across to show the inside.

Pr_2, Prostate Gland, outside view.

Sp, Spermatozoa, front and side views, greatly magnified. Set end to end it would take 500 to span an inch. Over 200 million spermatozoa are released in a single ejaculation.

INDEX

A

Abortion, 80

Affection, expressing mutual, by intercourse, 115

giving of gifts, caressing, etc., 55

After-play, 111

Aggressiveness, sexual, 40, 41

Allan, Edgar, 60

Art of love, 56

Aschheim-Zondek test for pregnancy, 79, 129

"Athletes, Sexual," 117

Attitudes and emotions in sexual relations, 55-60

affection, 55

confidence, 57

enthusiasm, 57

interest, 57

patience, 58

playfulness, 59

sympathy, 58

Awakening, sexual, 47-49

B

Beam, Lura, 123, 166

Blanton, M. G., 136

Smiley, 136

Blatz, William, 136

Bott, Helen, 136

Briffault, Robert, 36

Broadhead, Geo. L., 136, 166

Bromley, D. D., 82

Bryant, Louise, 82, 166

Burgess, E. W., 36

Buschke, A., 136

C

Cardio-vascular system and sexual ideas, 41

Caressing, 47, 94

value of, 49-50

Carey, W. H., 136

Children, 124-137

agreement for having, early, 124

eugenic considerations, 124-126

hindrances to having, 127-129

in the home, 132-136

planning for, 126-127

pregnancy, 129-130, 156, 158

Circumcision, 68

Clitoris, the, 63

and love-play, 97

stimulation, 110

Coitus interruptus, 143-147

Coitus, phases of, 93-111

afterplay, 111

copulative movements in, 107-110

entrance, making the, 100-102

foreplay, 93, 100

husband's problem:

premature ejaculation, 98

psychic impotence, 99-100

relaxation, 98

187

Gruenberg, B. C., 137
Guilt emotion, 51

H

Hamilton, G. V., 36
Harris, Frederic, 123
Hartman, Carl G., 82, 136
Heaton, C. E., 136, 166
"Heavy Petting," 153
Hereditary diseases and bearing children, 125
Highly sexed men, 151
Honeymoon, the, 72-83
  abortion, 80
  contraceptives, 77-79
  pre-marital examination, 80-82
  travel and favorable conditions for, 73-77
Hormones, 70-71
Hotchkiss, Robert, 136
Hunter, Dr. Allan, 155
Hutton, Isabel E., 112
Hymen, the, 64-65
  at first entrance, 96

I

Illness and sexual relations, 158
Impotence, psychic, 99-100
  temporary, 85
Incompatibility, sexual, 140
Inferiority anxieties, 52
  complex, 140
Instruction in technique of sexual intercourse, 84-112
Intercourse, sexual, 49, 52, 54, 91-93, 113-123
  after childbirth, 131
  during pregnancy, 131
  for conception, 114
  for expressing mutual affection, 115
  for releasing sexual tension, 115
  frequency problems, 113-123
    in later life, 121
  mutual adjustment, 118-121
  positions for, 102
  range of frequency, 117-118

Invitation to sexual intercourse, 91-93
Irving, F. C., 136, 166

J

Jacobsohn, F., 136
Jenkins, M. T., 40, 61

K

Kirsch, Felix, 24, 36
Kissing, 47
Kopp, Marie E., 67, 83, 123

L

Langdon, Grace, 136
Later life, frequency of sexual intercourse in, 121
Latz, Leo J., 83
Lewis, W. H., 71
Libido sexualis, 39
Loucks, G., 100, 112
Love, art of, 56
Love-marriages, 30-32
Love-play, romantic, 46
Lowie, R. H., 36
Lubrication, 95

M

Maladjustment, sexual, 23
  overcoming of, 138
Male sex organs, 68-70, 178-185
Malinowski, B., 40, 61
Man's sex organs, 68-70, 178-185
Marriage patterns, 23-36
  compound or group, 29-30
  love, 30-32
  matriarchal—mother family, 26
  patriarchal—father family, 27
  polygamy and communal, 27
  relationship, 35
  sexual factor in, 25
Married wisdom, 165
Masturbation, 144, 151-153
  and orgasm, 70
Matriarchal marriage, 26
Matsner, E. M., 83